on
Electronic Diagnostics

Volume 2

Published by
KELSEY PUBLISHING LTD

Printed in Singapore by Stamford Press PTE Ltd.
on behalf of
Kelsey Publishing Ltd,
Cudham Tithe Barn,
Berry's Hill,
Cudham,
Kent TN16 3AG
(Tel: 01959 541444).

© 1998
ISBN 1 873098 47 2

Acknowledgements

Our thanks go to Chris Graham who wrote this Electronic Diagnostics series and also to the expert assistance
provided by Frank Massey of Fuel Injection Services, Keith Derbyshire at Sykes-Pickavant,
Richard Keys at ATP Electronic Developments Ltd and Charles White of Equiptech.

INTRODUCTION

This is the second volume of our compilation of Electronics Diagnostics features from Car Mechanics. As before, we're aiming this book squarely at people in the motor trade, who can use it as a workshop guide to the characteristics, test procedures and typical faults found on common electronic engine management systems.

Each feature includes a full description of each system, an explanation of its characteristics (including all the code reader/self-diagnostic functions), the test gear needed, plus an all-important full circuit diagram.

Chris Graham and Frank Massey (Britain's leading expert on diagnostics) also identify, in clear and easy to follow terms, the usual faults found with each system, their symptoms and cures. This information will place you in a very strong position to help your customers. You should also recoup the purchase price very quickly...

We intend that this volume will be part of what will eventually build into a full diagnostics library..

Peter Simpson
Editor

Please note that any prices and telephone numbers quoted were accurate when the articles were first printed but may have changed subsequently.

ELECTRONIC DIAGNOSTICS – INDEX

PREPARATION

Basic Equipment	Vol 1
Management Systems (a Mugs Guide to)	Vol 1
Engine Control & Running Systems (A Basic Introduction)	Vol 1
Oscilloscope and Basic Preparation	Vol 1

SYSTEMS

Audi 80 (Bosch KE-Motronic)	Vol 2
BMW 3 & 5 series (Bosch Motronic)	Vol 2
BMW 3 & 5 Series (Bosch Motronic M1.7)	Vol 1
Citroen AX (Bosch MA 3.0)	Vol 2
Fiat Punto 1.2 (Weber-Marelli 6F)	Vol 2
Ford (Zetec)	Vol 1
Ford Escort Cosworth (Weber IAW)	Vol 2
Ford Fiesta & Escort (EEC-IV KAM)	Vol 2
Ford Fiesta XR2i & RS Turbo (EEC-IV)	Vol 1
Ford Granada 2.9i (EEC-IV)	Vol 1
Ford Sierra & Granada 2.0i	Vol 1
Honda Civic 1.6 (PGM-FI)	Vol 2
Honda V6 Legend (PGM-FI)	Vol 1
Jaguar 3.6 (Lucas 9CU)	Vol 2
MGF (MEMS)	Vol 2
Nissan Micra 16v (ECCS)	Vol 2
Nissan Primera (ECCS)	Vol 2
Peugeot 205, 309 & 505 GTis (Bosch LE2)	Vol 1
Peugeot 405 1.8i (Bosch Motronic MP5.1)	Vol 2
Peugeot 405 Mi16 (Bosch Motronic)	Vol 1
Range Rover	Vol 2
Renault Clio 1.2 (Bosch Monopoint)	Vol 1
Renault Laguna 2.0 (Renix/Bendix R)	Vol 2
Rover (from 1980) (Lucas)	Vol 1
Rover (Lucas EFI)	Vol 1
Rover 214 & 414 1.4 (MEMS SPI)	Vol 1
Rover 800 (PGM-FI)	Vol 1
Rover 820 (Lucas)	Vol 2
Rover 820 16v (MEMS)	Vol 1
Saab 900 (non turbo) & 9000 (Bosch LH)	Vol 2
Vauxhall (Ecotec)	Vol 2
Vauxhall 1.8i (Bosch LE3)	Vol 2
Vauxhall 24v Straight six	Vol 1
Vauxhall 2.0 16v (Bosch Motronic 2.5)	Vol 1
Vauxhall Astras, Cavaliers & Carltons 2.0i (Motronic)	Vol 1
Volkeswagen Golf MkII GTi (VAG Digifant)	Vol 2
Volkswagen 1.8 Golf & Jetta GTis (Digifant)	Vol 1
Volvo 940 2.0	Vol 2

SUPPLEMENT

Multimeters and Diagnostics	Vol 1

CONTENTS

Audi 80 (Bosch KE-Motronic) 25

BMW 3 & 5 series (Bosch Motronic) 69

Citroën AX (Bosch MA 3.0) 73

Fiat Punto 1.2 (Weber-Marelli 6F) 65

Ford Escort Cosworth (Weber IAW) 91

Ford Fiesta & Escort (EEC-IV KAM) 29

Honda Civic 1.6 (PGM-FI) 13

Jaguar 3.6 (Lucas 9CU) 21

MGF (MEMS) 87

Nissan Micra 16v (ECCS) 51

Nissan Primera (ECCS) 77

Peugeot 405 1.8i (Bosch Motronic MP5.1) 55

Range Rover 9

Renault Laguna 2.0 (Renix/Bendix R) 83

Rover 820 (Lucas) 17

Saab 900 (non turbo) & 9000 (Bosch LH) 39

Vauxhall (Ecotec) 47

Vauxhall 1.8i (Bosch LE3) 33

Volkswagen Golf MkII GTi (VAG Digifant) 43

Volvo 940 2.0 59

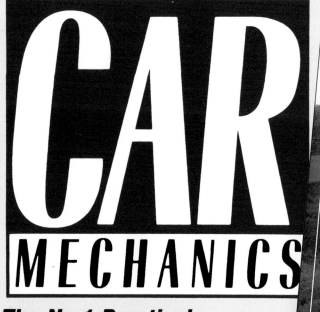

CAR MECHANICS

The No.1 Practical Magazine for Modern Car Enthusiasts & The Trade

Car Mechanics is now Britain's only monthly DIY motoring magazine for modern car owners. **Car Mechanics** also caters extensively for the independent motor trade with in-depth technical information.

Edited by Peter Simpson, with regular contributions from Rodney Jacques, Chris Graham, Jim Patten, Kim Henson and many other well-known motoring writers.

No.1 PRACTICAL MAGAZINE FOR MODERN CAR ENTHUSIASTS & THE TRADE   FEBRUARY 1999 £2.50

WIN! Clarke MIG WELDERS WORTH OVER £600

CITROEN BX CAMBELT SWAP

LIGHT UP! Adding extra brightness

E253 CVW

MONDEO PROJECT Cooling system repairs

GUNSON'S DIAGNOSTIC GEAR PROFILED

SCREWDRIVERS Choose the best!

PLUS: XANTIA PARTS PRICE GUIDE, PEUGEOT 106 SERVICE, MAZDA MX5 PROJECT

● Three major project cars in each issue – currently including a high-mileage Ford Mondeo, an accident-damaged Mazda MX5 and a bargain-basement, £650 MkIII Granada Scorpio.

● Electronic Diagnostics: Each month we take a popular model or group of models with the same engine management, and explain how to diagnose electronic faults and cover the usual weaknesses.

● Nine pages of free advice on readers' own technical problems each month.

● Regular features lifting the lid on the things that are going wrong with modern cars in the field, things that motor manufacturers often don't want you to know about!

● Tool and equipment tests. The latest gear put through its paces by experts who tell the whole truth!

Plus regular advice on auto-electrical faults, mechanical overhaul, bodywork repair, rustproofing, servicing and all the latest news.

GET 14 ISSUES FOR THE PRICE OF 12

CAR MECHANICS SUBSCRIPTION

To: KELSEY PUBLISHING LTD, PO BOX 13, WESTERHAM, KENT TN16 3WT. Tel: 01959 541444.

Please send me:
1 year's subscription (14 issues) to
Car Mechanics at **£29.50** UK & Eire ❏
　　　　　　　　£35.00 European mainland ❏
　　　　　　　　£41.00 Rest of the World (airlifted) ❏

I enclose my cheque for £ _____
(payable to Kelsey Publishing Ltd)

(Or) I wish to pay by MasterCard ❏ / VISA ❏ / AMERICAN EXPRESS ❏ / SWITCH ❏

No: _____

Expiry date: _____ Signature: _____ Switch Issue No: _____

Name: ....

Address: ....

....

....

..............................Post Code: ....

Daytime Tel. No: ....

ELECTRONIC DIAGNOSTICS!

How to trace faults in electronic engine management systems

Number 21: Nobody disputes the Range Rover's hard-won reputation for off-road excellence but what of its electrics? Chris Graham discovers that the mighty beast has its weaknesses.

The Rover 3.5-litre V8 must be one of the most durable, reliable and versatile motors around. It's been with us for years and is still going strong today, albeit in modified form.

With the advent of fuel-injection came the need for an electronic management system to harmonise fuelling

TYPICAL FAULTS
1. **General misfires 1**
2. **General misfires 2**
3. **Engine cut-out**

and ignition timing while maximising performance and economy. In the late

1980s Lucas 4CU was chosen for this task on Range Rover applications and, despite some pronounced weaknesses, didn't do a bad job.

Frank Massey (Fuel Injection Services, Tel: 01772 201597) has had plenty of experience with this set-up and is well aware of the pitfalls. Many of the faults which are likely to occur

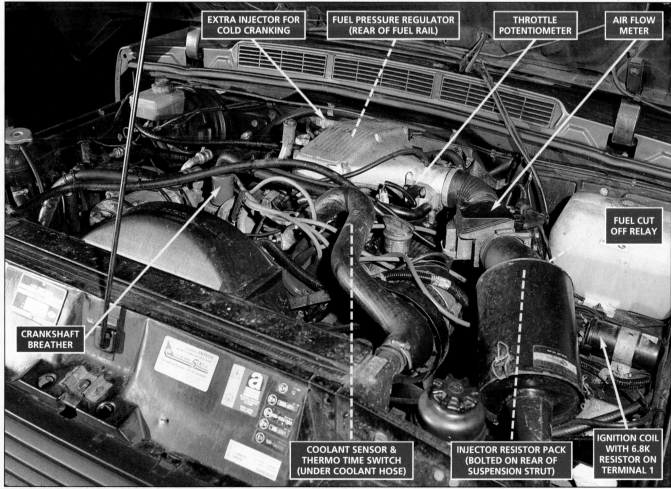

EXTRA INJECTOR FOR COLD CRANKING

FUEL PRESSURE REGULATOR (REAR OF FUEL RAIL)

THROTTLE POTENTIOMETER

AIR FLOW METER

FUEL CUT OFF RELAY

CRANKSHAFT BREATHER

COOLANT SENSOR & THERMO TIME SWITCH (UNDER COOLANT HOSE)

INJECTOR RESISTOR PACK (BOLTED ON REAR OF SUSPENSION STRUT)

IGNITION COIL WITH 6.8K RESISTOR ON TERMINAL 1

ENGINE MANAGEMENT

The Lucas 4CU management system is based around a 35-pin ECU (later versions had many more pins). Initially it may appear to be a complicated system but in reality it is fairly basic.

The fuel pump is mounted internally within the tank although there is no access through the floorpan – the tank has to be dropped to get at it which is usually a extremely messy job on a 'working' Range Rover.

The pump supplies high pressure fuel through a filter which is sited under the O/S wheelarch – a dirty location which can promote neglect. The fuel rail at the engine forms a ring circuit supplying the eight injectors. Pressure is controlled by a regulator on the return circuit.

The electronic components present consist of: the ECU (under driver's seat together with all main relays); a Bosch air flow meter (vane type) with two extra pins – linked to a safety-related micro-switch within the unit which activates the fuel pump during cranking/running; a coolant temperature sensor; an ambient air sensor and a throttle potentiometer.

In addition there is an auxiliary air valve (a bi-metallic strip valve heated electrically and from the engine block – provides extra air when engine is cold) and a cold start valve (an extra electronic injector which adds fuel spray directly into the plenum chamber but operates only during cold cranking – for a total of about twelve seconds).

The function of the plenum chamber is to provide expansion for the induction air and balance out irregularities. The cold start valve is controlled by a thermo time switch which is found next to the coolant sensor.

With this system, current is supplied to the injectors via a resistor pack. The injectors have a lighter wound coil than normal and are triggered by a 12V supply which is then dropped through the resistor pack to hold them open. The ground control comes from the ECU.

The injectors are switched twice per cycle – each delivery gives half the fuel required. During cranking additional injector pulses are provided (plus the cold start valve) and injection duration is extended too.

The trigger for the injectors comes from the coil so good ignition condition is essential for correct engine operation. On the ignition side there is a Limb-type coil which is mounted within the distributor and produces an AC sine wave. There is an amplifier unit mounted externally on the distributor body.

Note also that there is a series resistor (sometimes referred to as a ballast resistor) fitted to the coil negative terminal which links, through a fuel cut-off relay, to pin No.1 on the ECU. Frank says that this is a very important component and is there to protect the ECU from electrical spikes.

The ECU is easily damaged electrically and so this 6,800-ohm resistor has been included to guard against it. The engine will run without the resistor but the ECU will be at risk of serious damage.

From a diagnostics point of view Frank considers the Lucas 4CU system to be pretty straightforward. Apart from the AC waveform generated in the distributor, the only difficult signal to measure is injection duration. But these days, even this can be usefully tackled with an advanced multimeter.

Problems may arise with intermittent faults which can be very difficult to tie down. There is no code reader facility, no capacity for stored faults and no 'limp home' default – if an important component fails then the engine will probably stop! It has no ability to adjust its state of tune in an effort to compensate for component failure.

---

relate to poor connections caused, not surprisingly, by corrosion and dirt ingress. They tend to be intermittent and have any number of potential causes so accurate diagnosis can be a real headache.

One of the most common is a potentially serious fault stemming from an internal electrical failure within the ECU. Tracking this down and being sure about the cause can be tricky – repair costs will vary wildly depending on the conclusion. It is vital to be sure of your facts. Replacing an ECU when the real trouble is a rusty two-pin connector can be a disastrous mistake!

General preparation

First check for contamination within the induction system. There is a breather hose which runs from the o/s rocker cover and into the throttle body. At the engine end there is a small screw-in gauze filter which is often found to be blocked. Sometimes it may have been removed altogether, allowing oil to enter the throttle body.

Blocked or missing gauze filters should be replaced and the throttle body carefully washed. Contamination on the throttle disc must be removed after which adjustment should be checked.

Sometimes you may find that the throttle stop has been tweaked in an effort to compensate for a poor idle. This, however, detrimentally affects the throttle potentiometer voltage output and must be put right.

Frank advises that the procedure for this is to slacken off the potentiometer, set the disc to a closed position, 'crack' the stop so that the disc is held fractionally off the body, then set the pot. using a multimeter to 0.3V. This will establish a reasonably accurate base setting.

Inspect each of the eight spark plugs in turn. Don't fall into the trap of assuming that just because the first three or four are OK, all the rest will be too. These engines can suffer with bad injector fouling and plug condition is a good indicator of this. You must look closely at each one for signs of anything other that the ideal light grey deposit.

Because of the way in which the injectors are controlled, it is possible to get injector-related defects on individual cylinders. Misfires can be quite discrete with this engine because of its size – sometimes they can make minimal difference to running smoothness or performance.

Check all the vacuum hoses carefully – age leads to brittleness. There is one in particular, running round the back of the engine from the plenum chamber, which has a tendency to fall off, causing an air leak. Don't rely on lis-

The important but vulnerable resistor pack is found down here – below the air flow meter on the n/s suspension turret.

ELECTRONIC DIAGNOSTICS!

tening for characteristic hissing, the level of under-bonnet noise means that individual checks should be made.

Air leaks in the system are bad news and will lead to a weak mixture. Limited fuel adjustment is all that's possible, using the air bleed bypass screw on the air flow meter.

The resistor pack which governs injector firing is unfortunately located in the engine bay at the rear of the n/s suspension strut and is vulnerable to road dirt and moisture. It has a small 10-pin socket and Frank has seen many corroded examples.

Wash it out with carburettor cleaner and a stiff brush (not wire), lubricate and check for poor connections. The round pins often work loose so check and tighten all with a jeweller's screwdriver.

Also cast an eye over the fuel cut off relay which is found next to the coil. This can suffer with poor connections as well and is the component to which the important anti-spike resistor is wired.

Use a multimeter to check the output from the throttle potentiometer. Carefully sweep across the range and make sure there is no breakdown – should record about 0.3V shut, about 4.5V fully open. If you find it wrong make sure that the supply is good before thinking about replacement.

Tracing trouble

One of the most common problems associated with the Lucas 4CU-managed Rover V8 relates to misfires. Most are usually fuel-related and have little to do with ignition – but always check the electrical side nonetheless.

In most cases the misfires will be intermittent initially but will gradually get worse. Normally Frank finds the cause is poor injector triggering or no triggering at all – there will be a spark at the plug but no fuel for it to ignite. Most commonly faults like this will be caused by dirt on the resistor pack terminals.

Another possibility is that one of the control resistors has actually burnt out and no voltage is being supplied to a particular injector. So check the resistor pack using an ohm meter by measuring across the two input and the four output terminals.

Alternatively, switch on the ignition and measure the voltage supply to each injector. If this is non-existent then work back to the resistor pack, check that battery voltage is going in and that the output is satisfactory. If not clean all terminals and retry.

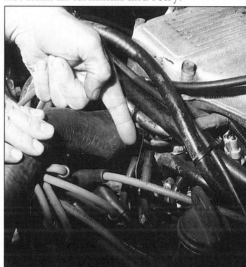

The coolant sensor and thermo time switch are both centrally placed on the engine, between the V banks and towards the front.

An injector blockage resulting in insufficient fuel delivery can be another cause of misfire. Inspection of the spark plugs should point to this (one or more 'lean' plugs).

ECU-related misfires are also a pretty common occurrence. The ECU's failure to switch the injector(s) long enough or consistently enough is often the cause, leading to a lack of fuelling.

The injection duration circuit within the ECU can suffer from two problems. Either it can fail to switch the injectors twice (often the second switch will be missing) so insufficient fuel is delivered or, it can break down completely, albeit on an intermittent basis.

Intermittent failure can occur under any conditions (light throttle, full load, cruise etc). The only way to diagnose satisfactorily this is by using an oscilloscope.

However, erratic misfire can also be caused by several other factors so don't automatically assume the ECU is at fault. There can be a defect in the ignition amplifier, particularly if spurious parts have been fitted. Always fit the latest spec. component if a new one proves to be necessary (about £50).

Alternators have been known to cause interference which can also lead

TECHNICAL SPECIFICATIONS

Throttle potentiometer	Supply	5V
	Earth	0.25V
	Wiper	0.3V static to 4.5V fully open
Coolant sensor	Supply	3.5V
	Output	3V cold, 1V hot
Air flow meter	Pin 39/36	Pump relay micro switch
	Pin 6	Ignition on – 4.2V
	Pin 9	Earth
	Pin 8	1.5V ignition on
	Pin 7	Pot. output – 3.6V static, 2.8V idle 4.5V with throttle fully open
	Pin 27	Ambient air – 3.3V
Resistor pack	Pin 9 & 1, 3, 5, 7 – 6 ohms	
	Pin 2 & 4, 6, 8, 10 – 6 ohms	
Fuel pressure	2.5 bar – no vacuum, 1.8 bar – with vacuum	
Fuel flow rate	80lt/hr	
Injector duration	14ms+ cranking, 10ms down to 5ms cold 2.5ms hot	
Injector trigger	Ignition pulse via relay and resistor to pin 1 at ECU	
Ignition timing	Approx. TDC but runs better at 6-8° BTDC	
Plug voltage	8KV at idle, 18KV snap load	
Coil output	30KV	

Exhaust emissions	CO	HC	CO$_2$	O$_2$
At idle	1%	300ppm	12%+	1.5%
At 3,000rpm	0.5%	100ppm	13-14%	1%

THE SERIES SO FAR

No.1   Basic systems – **July 1994**
No.2   Diagnostic equipment – **August 1994**
No.3   Test preparation – **September 1994**
No.4   Ford 2.0i – **October 1994**
No.5   Rover 200/400 – **November 1994**
No.6   Vauxhall 2.0i – **December 1994**
No.7   Peugeot 205/309 GTi – **January 1995**
No.8   Ford 2.9i V6 – **February 1995**
No.9   BMW 1.8i – **March 1995**
No.10   Vauxhall 2.0i 16v – **April 1995**
No.11   Rover 2.0i 16v – **May 1995**
No.12   Rover 1.6/2.0 EFi – **June 1995**
No.13   Rover 1.6/2.0 ignition – **July 1995**
No.14   Ford Zeta 16v – **August 1995**
No.15   VW 1.8 Digifant – **September 1995**
No.16   Honda Legend/Rover 800 – **October 1995**
No.17   Ford XR2i/RS Turbo – **November 1995**
No.18   Peugeot 405 Mi16 – **December 1995**
No.19   Renault Clio 1.2i – **January 1996**
No.20   Vauxhall 24v – **February 1996**

to misfires. Lucas have engineered replacement items to cure the problem so always opt for one of these genuine units.

Ensure that the internals of the distributor are correctly set up. Check, too, for internal seizure and/or loss of advance/retard weights. Distributor problems will cause erratic load control which will upset fuelling. It will also upset your bank manager as replacements cost about £400!

If the problem is traced conclusively to the ECU then all is not necessarily lost because it can be rebuilt. Frank says that the cost of this depends upon the extent of the internal damage – can be anywhere between £250 and £350. A new one will cost about £800 while a Lucas B90 replacement sells for about £450.

The third most common problem suffered by this Range Rover V8 application is engine cut-out, apparently related to fuel starvation. Unfortunately, once again there are several possible causes for this often intermittent problem apart from straightforward fuel pump failure (check the relay first).

The contacts for the fuel pump are mounted within the air flow meter and these can sometimes burn out. If this is the case then, ideally, the air flow meter should be replaced. However, Frank says that there is no reason why it cannot be modified to incorporate an additional relay into the circuit that replaces the internal points.

Before jumping to any wild conclusions check the contacts by probing both wires. Push the flap of the air flow meter open to close the points so that there should be no voltage drop across the contacts.

If the points have burnt out then one possible but not obvious cause can be a short to earth in the driver's

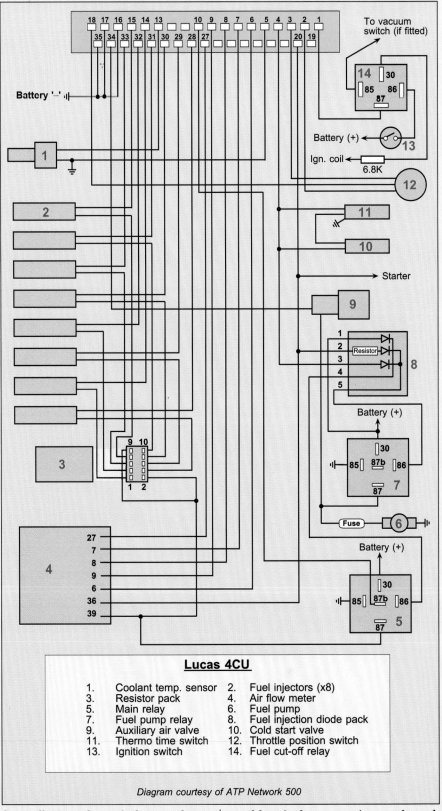

Lucas 4CU

1.	Coolant temp. sensor	2.	Fuel injectors (x8)
3.	Resistor pack	4.	Air flow meter
5.	Main relay	6.	Fuel pump
7.	Fuel pump relay	8.	Fuel injection diode pack
9.	Auxiliary air valve	10.	Cold start valve
11.	Thermo time switch	12.	Throttle position switch
13.	Ignition switch	14.	Fuel cut-off relay

Diagram courtesy of ATP Network 500

footwell. Here the main harness has a tendency to chafe against a securing bolt so check carefully.

Pay attention also to the wiring in the top of the fuel pump itself. If this is the problem then a new pump, complete with level indicator, is the only real option – about £150.

The socket into the pump is not particularly good. It can get hot and partially melt – Frank sometimes resorts to fitting his own termination block connector to get over this problem. The biggest nuisance with any fuel pump

problem is that access is so awkward. The tank has to be dropped which means, in most cases, that a tow bar will have to be removed too – normally rusted solid!

All in all, then, while the Lucas 4CU system is not particularly complicated itself, most common faults can have multiple causes which can make rectification a time-consuming and even infuriating business.

NEXT MONTH
Honda Civic 1.6.

ELECTRONIC DIAGNOSTICS!

How to trace faults in electronic engine management systems

Number 22: Chris Graham investigates the problems which can afflict the PGM-FI system used by Honda on Civic 1.6 models.

The PGM-FI engine management option – standing for programmed multipoint fuel injection – arrived on four-cylinder Honda applications late in the 1980s. It provides a complete engine management package, controlling both ignition timing and fuelling,

Frank Massey, proprietor of Preston-based Fuel Injection Services (Tel: 01772 201597) considers the sys-

TYPICAL FAULTS

1. **Loss of ignition**
2. **Loss of ignition 2**
3. **Lean mixture**

Car kindly supplied by:
Riding & Kok
Hartington Road
Preston, Lancs. PR1 8PQ
Tel: 01772 258862

tem to be generally durable and reliable. It features some subtle touches on the injection side, particularly with regard to idle speed control – these make it relatively refined and contribute to normally good levels of drivability and engine response right across the rev range.

Living with a Honda Civic is usually a fairly pleasurable experience from an electrical problem point of view. Frank

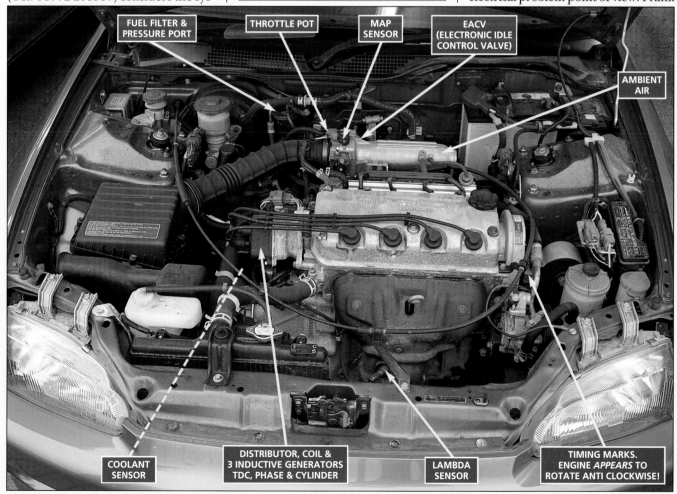

FUEL FILTER & PRESSURE PORT — THROTTLE POT — MAP SENSOR — EACV (ELECTRONIC IDLE CONTROL VALVE) — AMBIENT AIR

COOLANT SENSOR — DISTRIBUTOR, COIL & 3 INDUCTIVE GENERATORS TDC, PHASE & CYLINDER — LAMBDA SENSOR — TIMING MARKS. ENGINE *APPEARS* TO ROTATE ANTI CLOCKWISE!

ENGINE MANAGEMENT

We have covered the PGM-FI set-up previously in this series but not on a four-cylinder application – there are differences.

However, this version still relies on the three essential inputs for its operation. The ECU must receive data on engine speed, load and temperature before it can act.

A crankshaft position sensor relays engine speed information, a manifold absolute pressure (MAP) sensor measures engine load and a coolant temperature sensor in the water jacket reports on how hot things are getting. With this information the ECU calculates the relative ignition timing and fuelling settings which enable the engine to run at its most efficient whatever the driving conditions.

Other notable components include a throttle position sensor mounted on the end of the throttle spindle; an ambient air temperature sensor in the air induction manifold; a Lambda sensor in the downpipe (on cars with catalytic converters); an electronic idle control valve driven by the ECU and a heat-sensitive (wax) extra air valve for providing more air when the engine is cold. This combination provides very smooth idle response under all conditions and Frank has never yet seen a Civic suffering with idle surging problems of any sort.

The four fuel injectors are sequentially controlled through separate circuits and supplied with a voltage via a dropping resistor. They are lightly wound injectors and are opened by an initial voltage surge. A controlled voltage thereafter keeps them open for the desired duration.

A further refinement is that the MAP sensor is directly coupled to the manifold – most are connected by a length of pipe. The result is that reading delay is eliminated. The ignition signal is a 12V digital switch to earth from the ECU. It triggers an amplifier which, in turn, switches the coil.

The coil, together with a number of other important components, is built internally within the distributor. One problem with this layout is that it makes cranking or cylinder balance tests tricky because the engine cannot be cut out. The only solution is to attach a fly lead to the coil (negative terminal) by removing the cap. Frank says making a small, neat nick in the cap's lip with a round file will allow it to be replaced snugly over the lead and locked into place without hindrance.

On this application all the essential inputs required by the ECU, regarding engine position, TDC and camshaft phase, emanate from within the distributor. This is a unique feature to the Honda four-cylinder application and results in an impressive array of wires leading to and from the distributor – main power supply (ECU pin 15); a coil negative output to the tacho; signal generator outputs to the ECU including the TDC sensor (four pulses per cycle), the phase sensor (one pulse when cylinder No.1 fires) and the crank angle sensor which generates a multiple signal to denote acceleration and deceleration etc.

All these signals are produced as sine waves (about 10V peak-to-peak at idle) so an oscilloscope provides the only route to identifying their quality accurately. However, Frank says that most of these sensors are monitored by the comprehensive fault code system on this engine. Initial problems will be flagged by blink code to identify the cause but further investigation will require specialist equipment.

The self-diagnostic blink code used by the PGM-FI system is extremely accurate according to Frank. Any fault codes which are displayed can be relied upon. The first sign of any trouble is provided by a dash light which lights to indicate a current fault.

To discover where the problem lies you must check the blink codes displayed on the dash by bridging the service check connector found behind the passenger kick panel. Switch on the ignition and the light will flash fault codes. Long flashes equal 10s, short ones show 1-9. Codes are repeated after a two-second break.

Bear in mind that the power supply for this continuous fault code display system runs through a fused circuit so, if nothing shows, check the fuse first. Stored codes are cleared by 'pulling' the fuse which also initiates block learn from scratch – another feature of the system. It has the ability to re-write some of its control functions to compensate for wear or component deterioration. This works very well but, once initiated, the vehicle will have to be driven normally under all conditions before engine management will settle again.

To set idle speed switch ignition off, disconnect EACV plug and remove fuse 16. Set base idle by turning screw on throttle housing (faces offside). Reattach EACV, remove ECU control fuse (location may vary) to reset block learn, then drive car for 10-15 minutes.

Permanent faults will default the system into 'limp home' mode. Fuelling and timing will be compromised accordingly (slightly rich, slightly retarded) and idle may be slightly increased too. This can be a useful give-away to this condition.

Mixture adjustments are possible only on non-cat equipped cars, using a potentiometer which is found next to the ECU.

---

says that the cars rarely suffer from dirty, oily engines which makes actual electronic failure quite a rarity.

The plug leads are well routed out of the way of trouble and do not suffer with oil or water. Plug apertures normally remain dry and the distributor cap – central to efficient operation in this application – rarely suffers with dirt ingress. The throttle body, too, stays very clean and Frank puts this down to the fact that crankcase emissions are diverted straight back into the engine rather than through the body. Consequently, carbon build-up around the disc is not a problem.

The good news then is that the preparation work required by this engine before serious diagnostics can take place is negligible. There are exceptions, of course, but in the main initial checks can be confined to the obvious – loose hoses, wires, connections etc.

On the downside, from a practical point of view, the equipment required to tune this engine and investigate faults is specialised. Hand-held code readers are a non-starter; there is no facility for them at all. While it is true that the fault code system is comprehensive, taking things any further than simple identification will require an oscilloscope.

While serious faults are few and far between on this application there are some specific problems worthy of further explanation. The first two relate to ignition.

Loss of spark is a fault to watch for with this PGM-FI set-up. While straightforward to diagnose initially – no CB trigger coming from the distributor – tracking down the cause can be more involved.

Your first check should be with the ignition amplifier (found inside the distributor body). Originally the Civic

The black box on top of the throttle body is the MAP sensor. Immediately behind it is the throttle position switch.

ELECTRONIC DIAGNOSTICS!

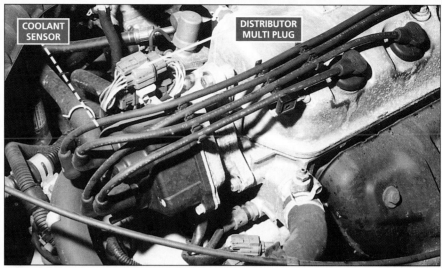

COOLANT SENSOR

DISTRIBUTOR MULTI PLUG

was fitted with a component made by OKI but this proved to be very unreliable. Frank understands that the problem was caused by HT induction, because the amplifier is located so close to the coil.

The solution is simple. An alternative amp from Hitachi was the official cure but not all cars got the treatment. Actually checking which is fitted can be awkward and you may well need a torch and a small mirror to make sure. The Hitachi unit will cost about £70 and should prove completely reliable.

Even if there is no fault Frank advises that any OKI amplifiers should be replaced anyway because it is almost certain to fail in the future. When fitting be careful because there are four connections to be made. Make a note of the terminations before removing the original component so that you get everything round the right way.

However, loss of spark is not always caused by amplifier failure. Another relatively common cause can relate to the speed sensing coil which is also found inside the distributor. This is mounted around the rotor and can work loose and come adrift with age. The worst scenario is that the rotor will chafe through the coil windings, destroying the crank angle output information to the ECU in the process.

To check this out fully it is probably best to remove the distributor – this also makes dealing with the amplifier easier. Just three bolts secure the component although Frank advises that marking the body and block to aid refitting is a sensible precaution.

Unfortunately, if the coil has been damaged in this way it is probable that a complete new distributor will be required. With a retail price of about £250 this is not good news.

Normally this engine management application works very efficiently as far as fuelling is concerned, particularly on cars with catalysts and closed-loop emission control. Nevertheless, all can suffer with a lean mixture which will upset idle control and emission levels – HC goes high and CO drops very low.

The problem, if it occurs at all, is normally more pronounced on earlier, non-cat models. Frank says that much of the trouble is caused in this case by technicians not realising that there is any potential for emission adjustment at all.

Control is via the mixture adjust pot. (located next to the ECU in the n/s footwell). With time it is almost inevitable that this will need to be readjusted. Frank says that alteration should be made in conjunction with the normal tune-up procedure.

The problem can be compounded by injector fouling – another age-related complaint. Couple this with a lean mixture adjustment and the result will be excess oxygen and popping in the exhaust.

If the mixture responds correctly to adjustment at the pot. then no further action is required. If not, then it is likely that the injectors are suffering from partial blockage. They will have

TECHNICAL SPECIFICATIONS

MAP sensor (ECU pin 26)	Supply	5V
	Output	3V at atmospheric pressure
		1V 20in/Hg (idle)
	Earth	0.25V
Coolant sensor (ECU pin 31)	Supply	5V
	Output	1V hot, 3V cold
	Earth	0.25V
Ambient air sensor (ECU pin 23)	Supply	5V
	Output	2.75V
Atmos. press. sensor (ECU pin 25)	Supply	5V
	Output	Variable with altitude/pressure (2.5V)
Distributor	TDC sensor – 4 x 360°, 10V AC peak to peak
	Cylinder ID – 1 x 360°, 10V AC peak to peak
	Crank sensor – multiple pulses, 10V AC peak to peak
Mixture potentiometer (ECU pin 20)	Supply	5V
	Output	1- 4V
Throttle potentiometer (ECU pin 24)	Supply	5V
	Output	0.3V closed, 4.5V open
Injector duration	2.5ms hot, 4ms cold, 8-10ms cranking
Ignition timing	18° BTDC at idle
Coil output	Max. 40KV
Plug voltage	12-15KV at idle, 18-20KV snap load

Emissions	CO	HC	CO_2	O_2
Cat-equipped	0%	0%	14%+	0%
Non-catalyst	1%	100-200ppm	13%+	0.5%

THE SERIES SO FAR

No.1   Basic systems – **July 1994**
No.2   Diagnostic equipment – **August 1994**
No.3   Test preparation – **September 1994**
No.4   Ford 2.0i – **October 1994**
No.5   Rover 200/400 – **November 1994**
No.6   Vauxhall 2.0i – **December 1994**
No.7   Peugeot 205/309 GTi – **January 1995**
No.8   Ford 2.9i V6 – **February 1995**
No.9   BMW 1.8i – **March 1995**
No.10   Vauxhall 2.0i 16v – **April 1995**
No.11   Rover 2.0i 16v – **May 1995**
No.12   Rover 1.6/2.0 EFi – **June 1995**
No.13   Rover 1.6/2.0 ignition – **July 1995**
No.14   Ford Zeta 16v – **August 1995**
No.15   VW 1.8 Digifant – **September 1995**
No.16   Honda Legend/Rover 800 – **October 1995**
No.17   Ford XR2i/RS Turbo – **November 1995**
No.18   Peugeot 405 Mi16 – **December 1995**
No.19   Renault Clio 1.2i – **January 1996**
No.20   Vauxhall 24v – **February 1996**
No.21   Range Rover V8 – **March 1996**

The oxygen sensor on this cat-equipped car is a four-wire, heated component.

to be removed and professionally cleaned ultrasonically.

If the car is fitted with a catalyst then the consequence of a lean mixture is that the oxygen sensor will try to correct matters by sending a permanent 'go rich' signal to the ECU. The block learn capability may then detect this constant signal and initiate a longer injector duration to compensate. This will work the cat harder and may even lead to MoT test failure.

Finally, Frank advises that if the injectors are removed for cleaning, or if any other tuning work is carried out on this system, the control fuse for the permanent supply to the ECU should be pulled out to re-activate block learn. It is important that new control values are installed after this sort of remedial work.

Thanks to Frank Massey, Network 500 and Sykes-Pickavant for their help with this feature. Frank runs two-day diagnostic courses – DIY to dealership technician – from £190 + VAT. Call 01772 201597 for details.

NEXT MONTH
Rover 820e (single point).

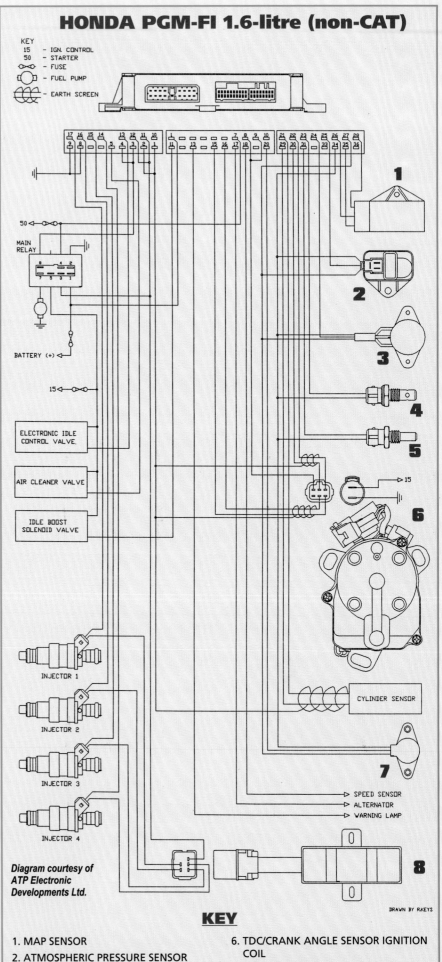

HONDA PGM-FI 1.6-litre (non-CAT)

KEY
15 – IGN. CONTROL
50 – STARTER
– FUSE
– FUEL PUMP
– EARTH SCREEN

Diagram courtesy of ATP Electronic Developments Ltd.

DRAWN BY R.KEYS

KEY

1. MAP SENSOR
2. ATMOSPHERIC PRESSURE SENSOR
3. THROTTLE POTENTIOMETER
4. AIR TEMPERATURE SENSOR
5. COOLANT TEMPERATURE SENSOR
6. TDC/CRANK ANGLE SENSOR IGNITION COIL
7. IDLING MIXTURE ADJUSTMENT SENSOR (IIMA)
8. INJECTOR RESISTORS

ELECTRONIC DIAGNOSTICS!

How to trace faults in electronic engine management systems

Number 23: Chris Graham unravels the frailties of the Lucas-controlled single point engine management system used by Rover on the early 820s.

The late 1980s Rover 820 has a reputation for trouble. Whether in 'E' or 'SE' form, the car's engine and its management system strike fear into the hearts of potential buyers. Is this justified?

In short, yes, according to Frank Massey, proprietor of Fuel Injection Services (Tel: 01772 201597). Unfortunately the prospects for DIY fiddling

TYPICAL FAULTS
1. **Engine running rich**
2. **Non-runner**
3. **Poor starting**

are limited on this application – specialist equipment is required for comprehensive fault correction.

The system has not aged particularly well and so problems can now be

many and varied. It was over-complicated at its introduction in the mid-1980s and suffers all the more for that today says Frank.

Reliance on a large, single fuel injector mounted within a conventional-looking throttle body, leads to problems. The unit is prone to snagging and becomes 'lazy' with age. Response becomes sluggish and emission levels can rocket.

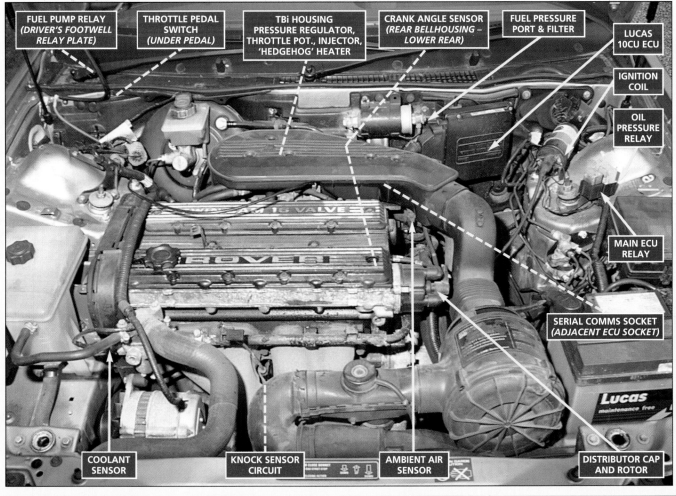

FUEL PUMP RELAY *(DRIVER'S FOOTWELL RELAY PLATE)*

THROTTLE PEDAL SWITCH *(UNDER PEDAL)*

TBi HOUSING PRESSURE REGULATOR, THROTTLE POT., INJECTOR, 'HEDGEHOG' HEATER

CRANK ANGLE SENSOR *(REAR BELLHOUSING – LOWER REAR)*

FUEL PRESSURE PORT & FILTER

LUCAS 10CU ECU

IGNITION COIL

OIL PRESSURE RELAY

MAIN ECU RELAY

SERIAL COMMS SOCKET *(ADJACENT ECU SOCKET)*

COOLANT SENSOR

KNOCK SENSOR CIRCUIT

AMBIENT AIR SENSOR

DISTRIBUTOR CAP AND ROTOR

ENGINE MANAGEMENT

The system relies primarily on engine speed and position information from a crank angle sensor in the bellhousing. It picks up from a phonic wheel on the flywheel to generate an AC waveform which is fed to the Lucas 10CU control unit.

This ECU provides complete engine management – ignition and fuelling control is combined. Another vital input comes from a MAP (manifold absolute pressure) sensor which is built in to the ECU and monitors engine load. It is connected to the induction manifold via a single vacuum pipe which transmits vacuum pressure.

Other components include: a standard NTC coolant sensor (found next to the thermostat housing); an ambient air sensor normally found behind one of the headlamps or near the battery; a throttle potentiometer mounted on the throttle body shaft to indicate throttle position; a stepper motor which indexes the mechanical linkage of the throttle disc to provide automatic idle speed control; an air temperature sensor (within the air induction hose – monitoring actual inducted air temperature; a knock control sensor mounted at the front of the block and providing sequential knock control to retard the ignition as necessary.

Inside the car there is a throttle switch behind the accelerator pedal. This dated component can cause problems – bent linkages or ruffled carpet can affect its operation. Its function is simply to inform the ECU when the driver releases the throttle. More modern systems incorporate this within the main throttle assembly.

Remember not to rev the engine from under the bonnet because the ECU will be confused into thinking that the throttle is still closed and the engine will run lean and erratically.

There is a traditional ignition system with standard coil, distributor cap and rotor. The fuel pump is mounted within the tank and pressure regulation is achieved using an integral unit within the throttle body assembly. Control for the pump is via a complex electrical circuit and problems with this can be a nightmare to put right.

In fact there are two completely different circuits used – the choice between then relates to chassis number (turning point is No. 177121). Essentially there is protection for the fuel pump through the oil pressure warning system – if the dash light comes on then the pump is stopped. There is also a separate pump relay.

For the pump to run both its relay and the main ECU relay must perform correctly. Further control comes from an inertia switch which cuts the pump in the event of an accident and its supply arrives through a ballast wire. The relays rely on good earths for their operation so ageing vehicles can have problems here.

An interesting feature is the spiked PTC or 'hedgehog' heater mounted within the inlet manifold. This is an electronically controlled component designed to warm the manifold during cold running – it assists with the evaporation of the fuel.

The system has a serial communication capability via a three-pin socket found near the ECU, close to the bulkhead. Not all serial communication systems can address this set-up, in fact most will not. Unfortunately all tuning adjustments must be made electronically so this can pose a problem.

Rover used a system called Cobest originally but now use one called Test Book. Fuelling is adjusted in this way and serial comms. also allow the stepper motor to be parked so that the throttle stop can be mechanically adjusted (to set base idle) together with its cable tension.

The big catch with this system is that it has a 'volatile' memory – everything programmable is lost if the battery is disconnected or allowed to run flat. The system defaults to a rich (5% CO or more) idle mixture which cannot be brought within current MoT limits.

The harsh reality is that problems with this engine are likely to be expensive to correct. Mechanical work will often be necessary which can send the cost of rectification soaring.

Preparation

There is a great deal to do on this engine. Start with the ignition. Leaking oil is often a problem. Removing the panel which covers the plugs will often reveal an oil lake – Frank has seen the plugs all but submerged in the worst cases! If you find this then really the engine should be stripped to cure the leak first.

The plug leads suffer with oil deposits too so must be cleaned. The horizontally-mounted distributor cap can suffer also with oil contamination – the seal at the end of the camshaft leaks.

All vacuum hoses are critical on this system because any drop in pressure will result in a rich mixture. Use a vacuum gauge to check actual load pressure at the ECU. This must be at least 18in/Hg and should be measured before doing any tuning at all. If it is low then consider air leaks, camshaft timing and valve seat condition as possible causes. Air leaks are usually caused by faulty vacuum pipes. Check all carefully and look for swelling and assess tightness of fit.

The most critical of all is the pipe which runs between the inlet manifold and the ECU. It incorporates a fuel trap to protect the MAP sensor and this should be checked and emptied. Check that the line is clear too but never blow down it towards the ECU.

Remove the air cleaner and wash the throttle body with carburettor cleaner. If the mixture shows more than 5-6% CO it is likely that the injector is dirty, assuming the vacuum pipes are intact. Ultrasonic cleaning and flow checking will often knock off 1.5-2%.

Other problems can be caused by the crank angle sensor, which is critical. Its location within the bell housing means that clutch dust, oil and grit can all lead to damage. The coolant sensor is another potentially weak link. Serial communication can present a failure here as 'engine too cold for tuning'. If you find this but the engine is obviously hot then coolant circuit failure is at the root of the problem.

Problem solving

The most fundamental problem with this system is its unfriendliness towards the DIY enthusiast. It can be difficult, confusing and expensive to deal with. Specialist equipment is required for any meaningful work and so the potential for home fiddling is limited.

One of the most common problems with this single-point management system is an over-rich mixture. Your starting point should always be the manifold vacuum because this pro-

Keep an eye on the condition and cleanliness of these two socket connectors. Both carry out important functions relating to the ECU circuitry. Watch particularly for chafing wires and poor contacts caused by corrosion/dirt deposits.

vides the key input to the ECU.

Another possible cause is that old favourite, the partially blocked injector. Other causes can be mechanical in nature, such as valve seat recession which is usually associated with high HC (1000ppm) emissions as well greater than normal CO readings. If a head overhaul is required the bad news is that it will cost about £800 including labour. A head gasket set alone costs about £130!

Once any vacuum or other mechanical faults have been put right it will almost certainly require a professional using the appropriate software to set-up the engine because of the specialist nature of the software involved.

One further consequence of a very rich engine is that the oil may well have become contaminated with fuel. This can lead to confusion as you endeavour to drive down injector duration to counteract the apparent richness. The result will be too short a duration and flat performance. If in any doubt change the oil and filter – always use good specification oil of the correct grade.

Equally common is an engine which will not run at all. This can be either fuelling or ignition-related. Crank angle sensor failure is a regular, as is a problem with the fuel pump relay. Because the crank angle sensor produces an AC signal it does require an oscilloscope to check its performance fully – output is about 10V peak-to-peak. While a digital multimeter can be used, Frank says that you still won't get a true

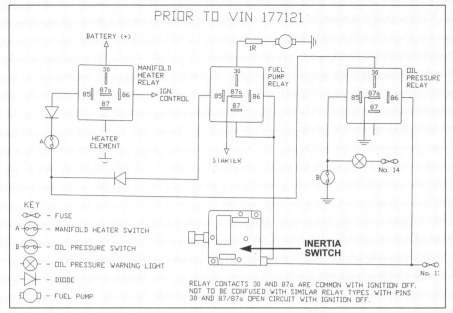

PRIOR TO VIN 177121

KEY
⊶ – FUSE
A ⊶ – MANIFOLD HEATER SWITCH
B ⊶ – OIL PRESSURE SWITCH
⊗ – OIL PRESSURE WARNING LIGHT
▷ – DIODE
⬚ – FUEL PUMP

RELAY CONTACTS 30 AND 87a ARE COMMON WITH IGNITION OFF. NOT TO BE CONFUSED WITH SIMILAR RELAY TYPES WITH PINS 30 AND 87/87a OPEN CIRCUIT WITH IGNITION OFF.

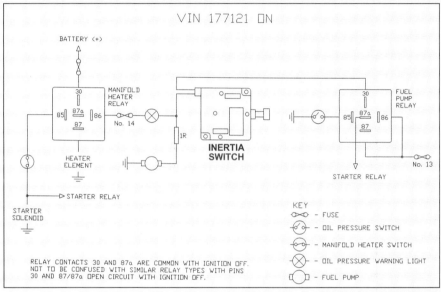

VIN 177121 ON

RELAY CONTACTS 30 AND 87a ARE COMMON WITH IGNITION OFF. NOT TO BE CONFUSED WITH SIMILAR RELAY TYPES WITH PINS 30 AND 87/87a OPEN CIRCUIT WITH IGNITION OFF.

KEY
⊶ – FUSE
⊶ – OIL PRESSURE SWITCH
⊶ – MANIFOLD HEATER SWITCH
⊗ – OIL PRESSURE WARNING LIGHT
⬚ – FUEL PUMP

value for the signal, or be able to see the clarity of each of the inductive pulses – both essential factors.

Assuming that the main relay is powered up, check whether or not there is a spark at the plugs. Frank is always wary of removing a lead to check for this in the old-fashioned way. He thinks it far less risky to use a strobe light with inductive pick-up on the leads.

If there is no spark at the plugs then work progressively back up the system. Check the coil lead to isolate the rotor arm – another common problem part. If all is well here then switch your attack to the dreaded fuel pump circuitry.

Fuel-related problems should be tackled in a different way. First check the inertia switch – an obvious cause often overlooked. You'll find this on the n/s of the centre console, usually behind a plastic trim or carpet-covered panel. It's easy to get at and has a red plunger on top. If this is up then the switch has been triggered. Push it down to reset.

If this is OK then go to the boot, lift the carpet and test the electrical feed to the pump itself. If there is none then you have problems because the fault will be buried deep within the complicated control circuitry already dis-

TECHNICAL SPECIFICATIONS

Crank angle sensor	Sine wave (peak to peak) between 4V-10V AC, subject to speed.
Coolant sensor	3.5V cold, 0.5V hot
Ambient air sensor	3-3.5V approx.
Throttle pot.	0.3V closed, 4.5V with open throttle (smooth transition)
Knock sensor	1-2V AC, amplitude subject to knocking
Fuel injector	2.5ms hot, 4ms cold, 8-10ms cranking
Fuel pressure	1.0-1.2 bar
Fuel flow	60-80 litres/hour
Throttle switch	Simple on/off voltage switch
Manifold vacuum	18-20in/Hg at idle 25in/Hg on over-run
Plug voltage	12-15KV at idle, 15-20KV snap load
Coil output	30-40KV
Dwell angle	10° at idle, 60-70° at high rpm
Ignition timing	Not adjustable – approx. 10° BTDC at idle

THE SERIES SO FAR

No.1   Basic systems – **July 1994**
No.2   Diagnostic equipment – **August 1994**
No.3   Test preparation – **September 1994**
No.4   Ford 2.0i – **October 1994**
No.5   Rover 200/400 – **November 1994**
No.6   Vauxhall 2.0i – **December 1994**
No.7   Peugeot 205/309 GTi – **January 1995**
No.8   Ford 2.9i V6 – **February 1995**
No.9   BMW 1.8i – **March 1995**
No.10 Vauxhall 2.0i 16v – **April 1995**
No.11 Rover 2.0i 16v – **May 1995**
No.12 Rover 1.6/2.0 EFi – **June 1995**
No.13 Rover 1.6/2.0 ignition – **July 1995**
No.14 Ford Zeta 16v – **August 1995**
No.15 VW 1.8 Digifant – **September 1995**
No.16 Honda Legend/Rover 800 – **October 1995**
No.17 Ford XR2i/RS Turbo – **November 1995**
No.18 Peugeot 405 Mi16 – **December 1995**
No.19 Renault Clio 1.2i – **January 1996**
No.20 Vauxhall 24v – **February 1996**
No.21 Range Rover V8 – **March 1996**
No.22 Honda Civic 1.6 – **April 1996**

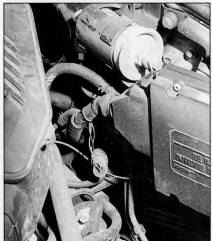

This three-wire socket in the centre is the connection point for serial communications. Unfortunately it is unlikely that enthusiasts will have much use for this. The software and equipment needed to access this system is expensive and so is effectively restricted to trade only. The thin pipe running behind the socket is the vital vacuum connection from the inlet manifold to the MAP sensor inside the ECU.

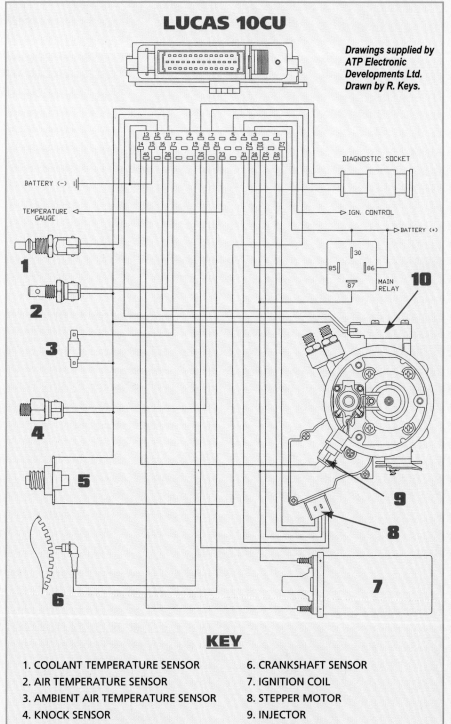

LUCAS 10CU

Drawings supplied by ATP Electronic Developments Ltd. Drawn by R. Keys.

KEY

1. COOLANT TEMPERATURE SENSOR
2. AIR TEMPERATURE SENSOR
3. AMBIENT AIR TEMPERATURE SENSOR
4. KNOCK SENSOR
5. THROTTLE PEDAL SWITCH
6. CRANKSHAFT SENSOR
7. IGNITION COIL
8. STEPPER MOTOR
9. INJECTOR
10. THROTTLE POT.

cussed. Best solution is to rewire with a fresh earth and supply line, using non-resistive cable. Include a separate, fused relay and build in a safety feature of your choice. Frank says this work will take a good auto electrician about two hours to complete – quite a lot of trim has to be stripped out.

You may also come across starting problems with this 820 Rover application. While the car may eventually fire, it might be obviously choked up and need to be revved to clear it. Part of the problem can be the use of incorrect spark plugs – resistive plugs should be used and Frank recommends NGK (No. BCPR6ES).

If you are dealing with a worn engine then manifold vacuum is almost sure to be down during cranking, making it harder to start than ever.

Under these conditions the temptation is to depress the throttle pedal in an effort to help but this will simply lessen the vacuum further – sending a 'go even richer' signal thus reducing the prospect of starting.

It is also worth checking the throttle stop. Somebody may have fiddled with it in an attempt to adjust idle control. The disc may not be completely shut which will have a detrimental, knock-on effect on starting performance.

Check the vacuum pipes too and make sure that they are the right diameter – this influences performance. Normally Neoprene microbore pipe is used (available from pneumatic pipe suppliers) with rubber connectors.

These ends are specialised and normally only sourced from a dealer. Replacing pipes and connectors can add one or two points of vacuum which may make all the difference.

Unfortunately, then, this system is not for the faint-hearted. It exhibits a complex combination of electronic and mechanical control with plenty of potential for failure.

Thanks to Frank Massey, Network 500 and Sykes-Pickavant for their help with this feature. Frank runs two-day diagnostic courses – DIY to dealership technician – from £190 + VAT. Call 01772 201597 for details.

NEXT MONTH
Jaguar XJ40.

ELECTRONIC DIAGNOSTICS!

How to trace faults in electronic engine management systems

Number 24: Chris Graham gets to grips with Jaguar's 3.6-litre straight-six to discover its electrical and tuning weaknesses.

Most people appreciate the engineering quality which Jaguar instill into their cars. They are built to last and, from a mechanical point of view, high mileage is not a problem assuming adequate maintenance.

The popular six-cylinder 3.6-litre variant of the AJ6 engine, used in the XJ6 and Sovereign (XJ40) models of the late 1980s, takes its instructions

---

TYPICAL FAULTS

1. **Poor, erratic idle**
2. **High CO emissions**
3. **Over-fuelling when cold**

Car kindly supplied by:
Amalco Gift Co.
Unit 3, Salter Street
Preston, Lancs. PR1 1NT

---

from a Lucas 9CU management system. This provides total engine management – ignition and fuelling are both controlled by a single ECU. There is no potential for ignition timing adjustment which is fully mapped but there is mixture adjustment (on non-cat models only) via a potentiometer on the air mass meter.

According to Frank Massey, proprietor of Preston-based tuning experts

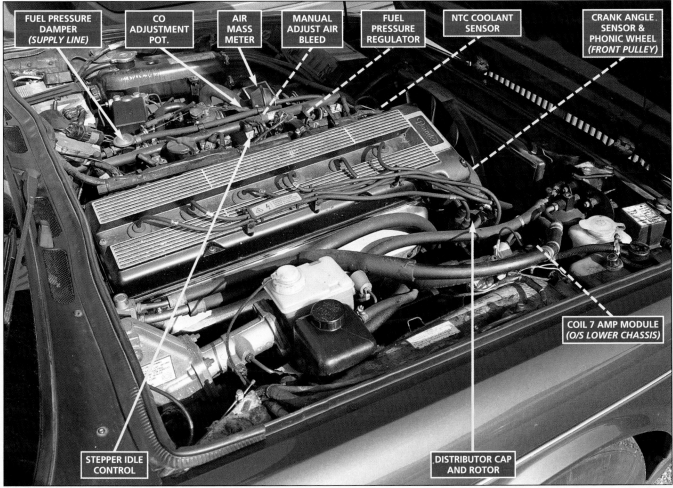

FUEL PRESSURE DAMPER (SUPPLY LINE) · CO ADJUSTMENT POT. · AIR MASS METER · MANUAL ADJUST AIR BLEED · FUEL PRESSURE REGULATOR · NTC COOLANT SENSOR · CRANK ANGLE SENSOR & PHONIC WHEEL (FRONT PULLEY) · COIL 7 AMP MODULE (O/S LOWER CHASSIS) · STEPPER IDLE CONTROL · DISTRIBUTOR CAP AND ROTOR

ENGINE MANAGEMENT

The key component in this system is the crank angle sensor. Everything is timed from this sensor's output so its role is vital. Unfortunately, its location at the front of the engine doesn't do it any favours. Being a magnetic component it attracts all and sundry and is therefore vulnerable to dirt and other contamination. It takes its input from a phonic wheel, mounted on the front pulley.

Other key components include: a straightforward two-wire NTC coolant sensor mounted in the thermostat housing; a hot-wire air mass meter providing engine load information; an adjustable throttle potentiometer mounted below the throttle body (access limited); a four-wire stepper motor for controlling idle speed – driven by the ECU in response to engine speed and output from the coolant temperature sensor. Some models may also be fitted with an auxiliary air idle control valve.

Also of note are: the NTC ambient air sensor mounted in the air induction system; twin control relays, one for powering up the ECU, the sensors and the injectors on the turn of the key, the other for the fuel pump which is brought to earth by the ECU.

The fuel system is straightforward with a high pressure, gravity fed fuel pump found under the vehicle to the rear (late version maybe inside the tank). The fuel rail and six injectors are very accessible which is good news. The latter, which are triggered just once per cycle, are controlled by three circuits from the ECU – paired off to reduce the electrical loading at the output stage from the control unit.

The ECU features a double edge connector (two sockets – see pic), both with independent harnesses. Frank thinks this is a good system. It allows for bigger pins – modern units have tiny ones which are more susceptible to damage and poor contacts plus are less able to transmit large currents. These sockets will help with engine identification if you are not sure which capacity you are dealing with. The 3.6-litre's unit features one black and one yellow socket while the four-litre has yellow and blue sockets. The two must never be interchanged – plugging in the wrong ECU will blow it.

The news on the DIY diagnostic front is not all good. Frank is not aware of any commercially available software for interrogating this 9CU system and believes this to be a dealer-only privilege.

However, the designers have included a fault code presentation system which we can all get at using a button on the dash. Located on the small control panel to the right of the steering column, the 'VCM' provides the key to the system. Switch off the ignition for five seconds, switch it back on to position two (do not start engine) then press the button. Any stored fault codes will be displayed with a two second pause between each. There are about 20 in all which, for some reason, range from 11 to 89.

Fuel Injection Services (Tel: 01772 201597), the system as a whole is fairly reliable but when there are problems it is the air mass meter which often provides the root cause.

Before we start, a word of warning. Do not confuse this system with that used to manage the 3.6-litre motor found in the XJ-S. This is a Lucas P-Digital system and no comparison should be made between the two. Also, bear in mind that outwardly the 3.6 looks very much like the 4-litre.

Preparation

Generally the 3.6-litre AJ6 engine is a pretty clean unit. Frank says that it is not particularly prone to oil leaks and so, although the plug apertures are deep, oiling around the plugs is not a typical problem. The leads generally fare well too. They are well-engineered and sensibly routed well away from direct heat – Frank has yet to change a faulty one.

There is nothing, apart from the rotor arm, to be found under the distributor cap. For this reason the cap is often neglected and rarely removed. So make a point of taking it off, checking for debris, corrosion and electrical erosion inside and cleaning it thoroughly. If the cap is badly contaminated inside then don't waste your time trying to clean it up – discard and fit a new one. Change the rotor arm too if fitting a new cap.

Remove the plugs and make the usual visual inspection. You should be watchful for obvious signs of fuelling imbalance between them.

There is a separate ignition amplifier mounted directly under the coil on the o/s inner wing, just behind the headlight. Both this and the coil are important components which can suffer with contamination. The most usual cause is the power steering reservoir which can be responsible for an oily residue over both.

The danger of this is that it will promote electrical tracking – not good news. The system produces a healthy spark of 35kV+ and you don't want this sort of output getting remotely near a passage back to the precious ECU.

Any oiliness should be washed off and then the components dried carefully. Check also the amplifier's socket. Frank says this can suffer from water ingress. The connector pins must be inspected in detail and, if needs be, cleaned and lubricated to ensure quality transmission.

The induction side of things on this engine is not too bad at all. The main air intake hose is large and makes a right angle between the air mass meter and the induction butterfly. It is not normally badly contaminated and is easily cleaned.

The stepper motor can be unscrewed simply for washing with carburettor cleaner. Be careful when refitting – the valve is easily damaged by the inexperienced. Make sure that it is fully retracted before refitting to avoid this risk. To do this connect up the stepper and switch on the ignition to

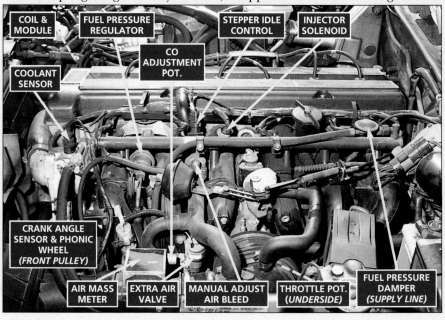

COIL & MODULE | FUEL PRESSURE REGULATOR | STEPPER IDLE CONTROL | INJECTOR SOLENOID | COOLANT SENSOR | CO ADJUSTMENT POT. | CRANK ANGLE SENSOR & PHONIC WHEEL (FRONT PULLEY) | AIR MASS METER | EXTRA AIR VALVE | MANUAL ADJUST AIR BLEED | THROTTLE POT. (UNDERSIDE) | FUEL PRESSURE DAMPER (SUPPLY LINE)

ELECTRONIC DIAGNOSTICS!

automatically drive in the valve, then refit.

It is worth checking the operation of the throttle potentiometer at this stage too. As standard its output should be 0.3V with the throttle closed. Any variation in this reading will cause problems. If you find this then first wash the disc carefully to remove any contamination which may be preventing it closing completely. Secondly, check the stop. It may have been badly adjusted.

If both are OK then you must suspect wiring or the potentiometer itself. Unfortunately, these components can become contaminated with oil which wrecks their output performance. Frank does not consider it worth attempting to wash one out – in his experience they never work properly after contamination. Replacement – for about £65 – is the only sure solution.

The fuel injectors are prone to fouling on this application but this can really be assessed only after carrying out the basic tune up, including mixture adjustment, and then observing exhaust gas analysis. Most Jags of this age will have covered a high mileage so expect to invest a little in restoring the injectors to peak performance.

Remember also that there is a gauze filter both front and rear of the air mass meter. If these are damaged or missing this will affect component performance. Both must be intact otherwise air flow rates are altered and so output will vary accordingly.

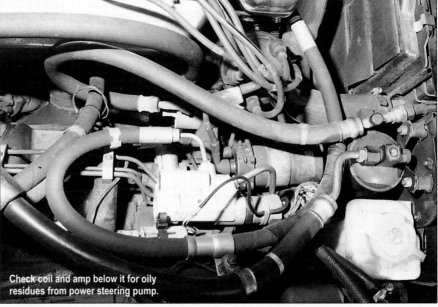

Check coil and amp below it for oily residues from power steering pump.

Jag jitters

One of the most common problems with these big cats is one of poor idle. If you find a car with lumpy tickover, popping through the exhaust and high HC emissions (600-700ppm) then there are several possible causes.

First suspect the injectors. These are easy to remove so testing is a relatively low cost operation. If they are found to be OK then switch your attention to the manifold vacuum.

On a good engine this should be about 20in/Hg. Readings lower than this should suggest induction air leaks and/or a problem with the tappets. Take vacuum readings from as many points in the manifold as you can – there are several at each end of the engine. You may well find low vacuum at one end which is not particularly noticeable at the other, so don't just make one test and assume all is well.

These engines can suffer from tight tappets for a number of reasons. Check the clearances first but, if this is not the problem, then the head will have to come off. This is bad news because it's technically involved and expensive. If the car has covered a very high mileage then Frank thinks it best to remove the head anyway so that the valves and seats can be thoroughly inspected. Obviously if there are problems here these must be sorted out before a decent level of tune can be achieved.

A vehicle suffering with high CO emissions is another relatively common occurrence. There is a potentiometer in the air mass meter intended for mixture trimming operations only. Normally this should be set mid-range (about 2.5V). If the mixture is erratic through the range – OK at idle but rich at cruise, or *vice versa* – it is likely that the air mass meter is at fault.

This component generates a variable voltage output dependent upon the flow of air passing through it. Tolerances can shift with age which will affect the output value and destroy the essential relationship between it and air flow rate.

Alternatively, it can suffer with electrical 'noise' on the output signal. This can cause real problems, even though the signal itself may well be fine. Identifying this with anything other than an oscilloscope is a problem. With a multimeter all you will read at idle is about 1.6V, which will be an averaged value effectively masking any interference.

The effect of noise on the signal is total confusion for the ECU. The result will usually be over-fuelling and poor running characteristics. Air mass meter voltage output is critical so a 'noisy' signal throws things completely.

In the worst cases it creates a switching signal which generates rich/lean mixture swings. A tell tale sign can be

TECHNICAL SPECIFICATIONS

Crank angle sensor	A/C waveform, 12V peak to peak dependent on speed. Cranking – 1.5-2.0V peak to peak
Air temp. sensor	Approx. output 3V, dependent on ambient temperature
Amp	5V output, square wave, from ECU pin No.1 + 4 (black connector)
Air mass meter	Max 0.7V static, 1.7V at idle 4.5V with throttle open (static test)
Auxiliary air valve	12V output, square switching via ECU pin No.20
Coolant temp. sensor	0.5V hot, 3.5V cold
Throttle pos. switch	0.3-4.5V with throttle open
Oxygen sensor	0.2-0.8V, switching at 1–3Hz
Injector duration	4ms cold, 2.8ms hot
Fuel pressure	2.9-3.2 bar, 0.5+ bar with no vac.
Coil output	35KV

THE SERIES SO FAR

No.1	Basic systems – **July 1994**
No.2	Diagnostic equipment – **August 1994**
No.3	Test preparation – **September 1994**
No.4	Ford 2.0i – **October 1994**
No.5	Rover 200/400 – **November 1994**
No.6	Vauxhall 2.0i – **December 1994**
No.7	Peugeot 205/309 GTi – **January 1995**
No.8	Ford 2.9i V6 – **February 1995**
No.9	BMW 1.8i – **March 1995**
No.10	Vauxhall 2.0i 16v – **April 1995**
No.11	Rover 2.0i 16v – **May 1995**
No.12	Rover 1.6/2.0 EFi – **June 1995**
No.13	Rover 1.6/2.0 ignition – **July 1995**
No.14	Ford Zeta 16v – **August 1995**
No.15	VW 1.8 Digifant – **September 1995**
No.16	Honda Legend/Rover 800 – **October 1995**
No.17	Ford XR2i/RS Turbo – **November 1995**
No.18	Peugeot 405 Mi16 – **December 1995**
No.19	Renault Clio 1.2i – **January 1996**
No.20	Vauxhall 24v – **February 1996**
No.21	Range Rover V8 – **March 1996**
No.22	Honda Civic 1.6 – **April 1996**
No.23	Rover 820 single point – **May 1996**

injector duration. Normally at idle this should be 2.5-3ms (engine hot) but this sort of problem can boost it to 5ms.

Noise on the line is caused by an internal defect within the air mass meter – its control circuitry suffers. Frank's advice is first to check for good supply and earth voltages. These are both vital values and if they are OK then the meter itself is probably at fault.

Frank says that Jaguar do produce a modified air mass meter for about £400 which has to be bought complete, with additional wiring harness adding a further £70 or so. The better news is that original units can be successfully repaired for about £250.

The third common problem with this engine is an over-fuelling condition when cold. This complaint has been the subject of a factory modification so the occurrence rate is obviously significant.

The symptoms are that you are unable to start the engine due to flooding. The way to clear it is to unplug all the injectors and crank the engine. It will eventually start and clear the plugs, after which the injectors can be re-connected.

The root of the problem lies with the coolant sensor which must be replaced. The modified unit from Jaguar – part No. DVC3728 – has a black plastic body and socket compared to the white plastic insulator on the original. Many will have been changed already but watch for those which have not.

In short then it's likely that high-mileage 3.6s will require some money spending on them from a tuning point of view. New owners should expect and budget for this expenditure to ensure continued reliable and efficient driving.

NEXT MONTH
Audi 80 Sport.

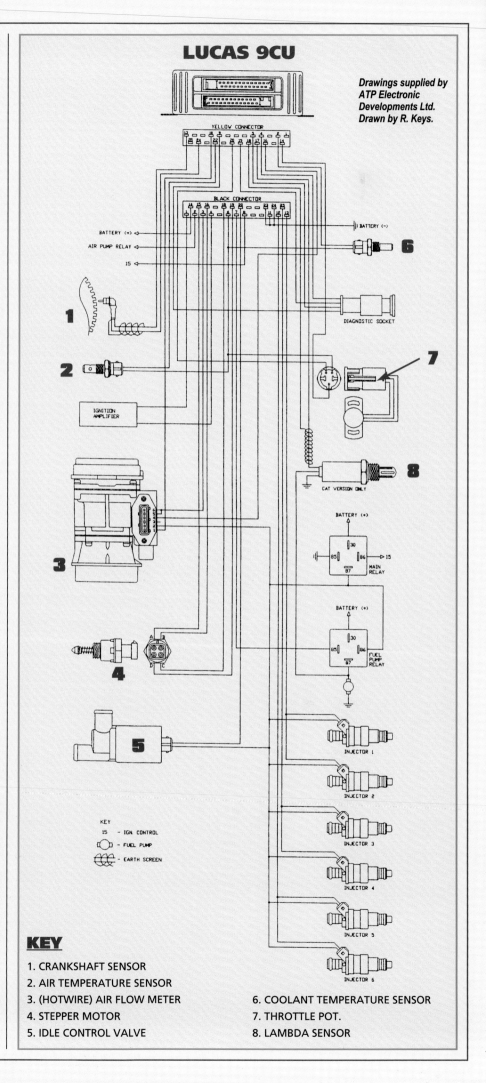

LUCAS 9CU

Drawings supplied by ATP Electronic Developments Ltd. Drawn by R. Keys.

KEY
15 – IGN CONTROL
– FUEL PUMP
– EARTH SCREEN

KEY

1. CRANKSHAFT SENSOR
2. AIR TEMPERATURE SENSOR
3. (HOTWIRE) AIR FLOW METER
4. STEPPER MOTOR
5. IDLE CONTROL VALVE
6. COOLANT TEMPERATURE SENSOR
7. THROTTLE POT.
8. LAMBDA SENSOR

ELECTRONIC DIAGNOSTICS!

How to trace faults in electronic engine management systems

Number 25: The Bosch KE-Motronic management system used by Audi on the late 1980s 80 models combines electronic and mechanical systems. There can be problems, as Chris Graham discovers.

The Bosch KE-Motronic management differs from most covered in this series because it uses electronic control to support mechanical fuel injection. It provides total engine management but with mechanical fuelling. Ignition is controlled by the ECU and so there is

TYPICAL FAULTS
1. **Stalling/cutting out**
2. **Poor idle quality**
3. **Poor starting**

no cross-over between this and the popular Jetronic system – the two have very few similarities at all.

The good news is that KE-Motronic is all but bombproof, according to Frank Massey of tuning experts Fuel Injection Services (Tel: 01772 201597). The bad news is that if prob-

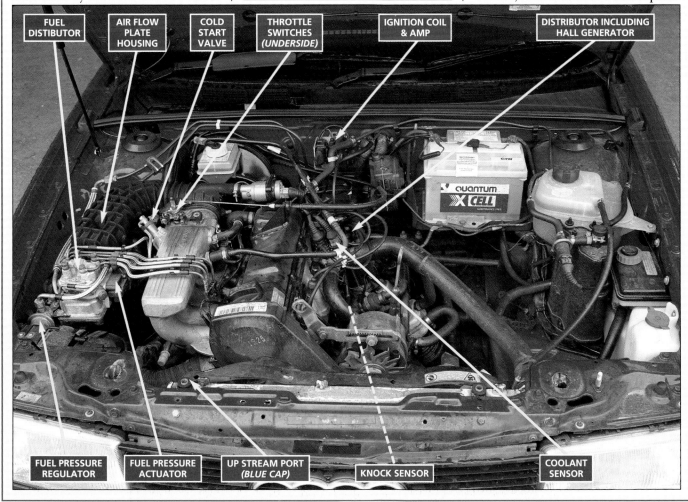

FUEL DISTIBUTOR — AIR FLOW PLATE HOUSING — COLD START VALVE — THROTTLE SWITCHES (UNDERSIDE) — IGNITION COIL & AMP — DISTRIBUTOR INCLUDING HALL GENERATOR

FUEL PRESSURE REGULATOR — FUEL PRESSURE ACTUATOR — UP STREAM PORT (BLUE CAP) — KNOCK SENSOR — COOLANT SENSOR

ENGINE MANAGEMENT

The system utilises a mechanical fuel distributor which delivers the petrol to mechanical injectors which are opened by fuel pressure. Consequently, the fuel supply pressure needed is very much higher than on other electronic systems. This provides an obvious potential hazard for the uninitiated.

It is essential when testing this system that although a basic multimeter can be used to good effect – the signals are not complex – you must have access to mechanical fuel pressure gauges. Correct pressure really is central to efficient working – without it good performance will not be possible.

The basics of the system are quite straightforward. There is a circular metal air flow plate attached to a beam. This is hydraulically damped and as induction air passes over the plate the beam is deflected and acts upon a plunger in the fuel metering head. This plunger is the controlling feature over the amount of fuel being delivered to the injectors.

The control of fuel delivery is rather more complicated. Frank does not think it's worthwhile detailing what goes on within the metering head because it is largely irrelevant from a tuning point of view. If faulty it will have to be replaced.

The system also features a catalytic converter so up-stream mixture measurements (ahead of the cat) have to be taken for meaningful results. Fortunately, Audi provide a convenient measurement point for this. After setting the mixture a reading from the tailpipe can be taken to establish that the cat is working as it should.

Other components include a high-pressure fuel pump which is normally gravity-fed and pumps at about six bar. There is also a high-pressure filter, after which the fuel passes into the metering head. A pressure regulator is used on the return circuit back to the tank.

There is a fuel accumulator which is a simple storage device intended to maintain an equal and even supply pressure from the pump – the last thing you want on this system is pressure pulses in the fuel supply. It also stores fuel pressure after switch off.

On the electrical side of things important components include a coolant sensor in the water jacket close to the thermostat housing; a signal generator (Hall generator) within the distributor provides the trigger for the ignition; a knock sensor; a single relay to power up the ECU; mechanical idle and full load contact switches – both mounted under the throttle (difficult

to access), and a Lambda sensor. This monitors oxygen content in the exhaust and its output enables the ECU to vary the voltage supplied to the fuel actuator, thus controlling fuel supply – mechanical closed-loop control.

In addition, there is a cold-start valve which is an electro-mechanical device (driven by the ECU) but this only works under conditions of extreme cold. Consequently, it is hardly ever seen to work in the UK – people often think of its inactivity as a problem but it's not. You'll also find a straightforward Bosch rotary idle valve which is directly controlled by the ECU.

Within the main metering head there is a throttle potentiometer which is not in fact attached to the throttle. It connects to the pivot on the air flow plate beam. This measures air plate deflection and output varies from about 0.25V at idle to around 4.5V wide open.

The ignition system is conventional, consisting of an amplifier module driven by a trigger from the ECU, mounted near the coil, the coil itself and the spark plugs.

There is scope for code reading. A terminal within the car (near the gear lever console) has to be shorted out to present blink codes on the dash. No code reader is required.

---

lems do occur then they are likely to be expensive.

The work involved is specialised and the important parts are pricey. If the fuel control electronics do fail then the system will revert to a failsafe which is in itself very capable – the change is virtually unnoticeable and normal driving is quite possible. However, it is fuel-related problems which cause the real headaches, as we'll see later.

Preparation

Begin by removing the large rubber bellows which fits over the air flow plate and link directly to the induction manifold. This will provide access to the plate itself – its position is absolutely critical for correct fuelling.

Some cars will conveniently have a sticker on the plate with instructions on how to set it up correctly; others will not. If this is missing then Frank strongly advises getting the manual on the system because measurements have to be made, preferably using a vernier gauge, and must be precise. The datum points involved are best explained in diagrammatic form which is where the manual comes into its own.

Setting up the plate can be an involved procedure. A small pin acts as a stop and will sometimes have to be driven into position using a small hammer and punch. Great care is needed because if you drive the pin in too far then the whole assembly has to come

apart so it can be driven back out – a few hours work in itself.

It is quite common to find that the stop position is incorrect – the continual action of the plate gradually knocks it out of place. Frank says that often you will find it fractionally out and, although this can normally be accommodated for through mixture adjustment (there is a screwed plunger acting on the beam to do this), you normally end up with a fuelling range which is out of specification.

The other possibility is that if the engine has suffered a backfire then the reverse pressure pulse could possibly damage or distort the air flow plate, causing it to foul on the body. Check for this by operating the disc by hand

through its entire travel. Be sure the plate rests at its 'zero' position as indicated in the manual.

Clean out the induction system too. Check the throttle body and wash both discs carefully. Remove the idle control valve, wash and lubricate it and check the idle contact it is making – without this various system functions will not operate correctly.

The distributor often suffers with dirt contamination. Remove the cap, check, wash and carefully dry before reassembly. The leads are of good quality but fitted at the plug end with a metal shroud on most models, which can become conductive. A possible solution is to replace with rubber-ended leads from BMW or Mercedes-Benz.

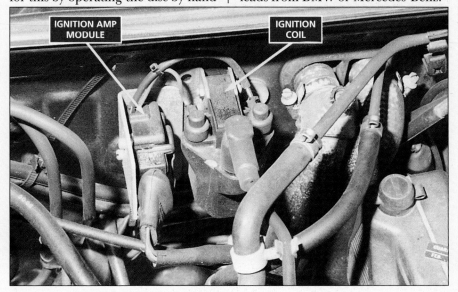

IGNITION AMP MODULE
IGNITION COIL

ELECTRONIC DIAGNOSTICS!

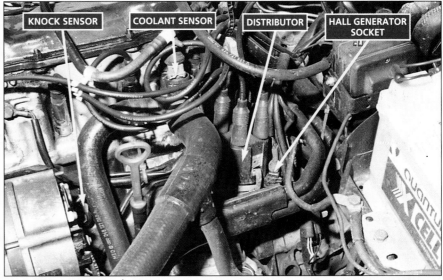

KNOCK SENSOR | COOLANT SENSOR | DISTRIBUTOR | HALL GENERATOR SOCKET

The system is critical of air leaks between the metering head and the induction manifold – any loss of air will affect the plate positioning so check this aspect with care as well.

Problem solving

If the car is suffering with cutting out after over-run, is difficult to re-start and when it does so runs rich, the main cause is without doubt a problem with the air flow plate.

This may have become contaminated or be sticking within the body. One simple reason for this may be a badly fitted replacement air cleaner. Sometimes the underside of this can interfere with the plate's travel.

Plates cannot be bought separately and Frank says that a complete replacement metering head is expensive. However, distorted plates can be straightened using a block of wood and a carefully-aimed wooden mallet (not a hammer because you will stretch and spread the metal and it will never fit).

The plate is held in place with a central bolt which should be bonded into position, so will need firm pressure to undo. It should be a perfectly flat disc and if in doubt use a straight edge to check for deviation. If the edge has become burred and you decide to dress these out with a fine file, be very careful. The worst thing you can do is create a flat, which will allow air past.

Frank's advice is that if you find any other problems with the metering head, you leave their correction to an experienced professional. If you get it wrong the entire fuelling of the engine will be corrupted. The head is screwed together so there is a temptation to take it apart and have a look yourself. Don't! In Frank's experience this always leads to a ruined component that will never function properly afterwards. The solution is to get the component professionally rebuilt or calibrated, depending on the problem.

Poor idle quality is another common complaint with this engine and management system. Assuming that it is not being caused by aged spark plugs, dirty distributor cap and/or HT lead problems which should normally be dealt during basic tuning procedures, the trouble may well relate to the injectors.

Normally the solution is to whip them out for cleaning using an ultrasonic cleaning bath. However, in this case Frank says that the injector design makes this approach ineffective. The opening and closing of the pintel is controlled by fuel pressure, rather than by an electric voltage. Because this form of control is not an option on standard cleaning equipment the injectors cannot be driven and are not cleaned thoroughly.

The best solution is replacement. Always use genuine Bosch injectors which cost about £35 each, depending upon application. Bear in mind that the problem will usually be masked during normal driving because of the higher fuel flow rate.

Another cause of idling problems is dirt in the system. This is serious because any physical contamination will cause havoc within the fuel meter. Disconnect various pipes around the fuel distributor and look for signs of trouble (deposits, rust, etc.).

Another good indicator as to the state of the system is to remove and cut in half the fuel filter. An examination of the contents of the element inside will show if it's been collecting a lot of dirt – some of which eventually forces its way onwards. The only remedy is to strip the whole system and flush it clean from the tank to the injectors – very expensive.

Problems with starting, either from cold or when the engine is hot, is an-

TECHNICAL SPECIFICATIONS

Coolant sensor	3-4V cold, 0.5-1V hot
Knock sensor	Approx. 1-2V output dependent on knock
Hall generator	5V digital centre pin, 12V supply, 0.25V earth
Idle switch (pin 28) Full load switch (pin 31)	Both simple voltage switches at each end of throttle travel.
Ignition trigger (pin 11)	5V digital
Oxygen sensor	0.2-0.8V @ 1-3Hz
Throttle potentiometer	0.5-4.5V (static to air flow plate fully open)
Idle control valve (pin 17)	12V digital, 100Hz
Ignition timing	18° BTDC with vac. (check specific data from engine code)
Pressure regulator	Check pressure with reference to voltage from coolant sensor
Fuel system pressure	6.1-6.6 bar
Differential pressure	Hot – 0.3-0.5 bar below system Cold – 1.3-1.6 bar below system
Decay pressure	20 mins, 3.2 bar
Fuel flow rate	90-120lt/hr
Emissions	
Up stream	CO 1% HC 100ppm, CO_2 13% O_2 1%
Down stream (after Cat)	CO 0.2-0% HC 50-0ppm CO_2 14-15% O_2 0.5-0%

THE SERIES SO FAR

No.1	Basic systems – **July 1994**
No.2	Diagnostic equipment – **August 1994**
No.3	Test preparation – **September 1994**
No.4	Ford 2.0i – **October 1994**
No.5	Rover 200/400 – **November 1994**
No.6	Vauxhall 2.0i – **December 1994**
No.7	Peugeot 205/309 GTi – **January 1995**
No.8	Ford 2.9i V6 – **February 1995**
No.9	BMW 1.8i – **March 1995**
No.10	Vauxhall 2.0i 16v – **April 1995**
No.11	Rover 2.0i 16v – **May 1995**
No.12	Rover 1.6/2.0 EFi – **June 1995**
No.13	Rover 1.6/2.0 ignition – **July 1995**
No.14	Ford Zeta 16v – **August 1995**
No.15	VW 1.8 Digifant – **September 1995**
No.16	Honda Legend/Rover 800 – **October 1995**
No.17	Ford XR2i/RS Turbo – **November 1995**
No.18	Peugeot 405 Mi16 – **December 1995**
No.19	Renault Clio 1.2i – **January 1996**
No.20	Vauxhall 24v – **February 1996**
No.21	Range Rover V8 – **March 1996**
No.22	Honda Civic 1.6 – **April 1996**
No.23	Rover 820 single point – **May 1996**
No.24	Jaguar 3.6 straight six – **June 1996**

other relatively common complaint. Frank says that the normal culprit is a combination of poor fuel pump performance due to wear – low pressure and supply rate – blocked or poor injector performance and/or what's termed 'fuel decay'.

The latter relates to the valves in the system which prevent fuel from running back to the tank. If these develop faults then excessive cranking is required to prime the system. Replacing these is not expensive but, as a practical interim measure, Frank suggests you can 'hard wire' the cold start valve so that it operates whenever the engine is cranked.

To do this you need a take-off from the starter motor and a direct earth to the other side of the cold start injector – this removes ECU control. The snag is that with the valve operating under all conditions you will have to be quick when starting to avoid flooding. The throttle has to be opened slightly during cranking but this should not be a problem if the driver is aware that a temporary fix is in place.

Alternatively, Bosch do a special relay (Part No. 0 340 000 003 085) which pulses the injector rather than constantly switching it. This can be wired in the same way but is obviously more expensive.

With any fuel-related problem on this system it is essential you have access to a pressure gauge to measure main system pressure as well as control pressure – the responsibility of the actuator. Refer to the spec table for the relevant pressure values.

NEXT MONTH
Ford Escort/Fiesta 1.4

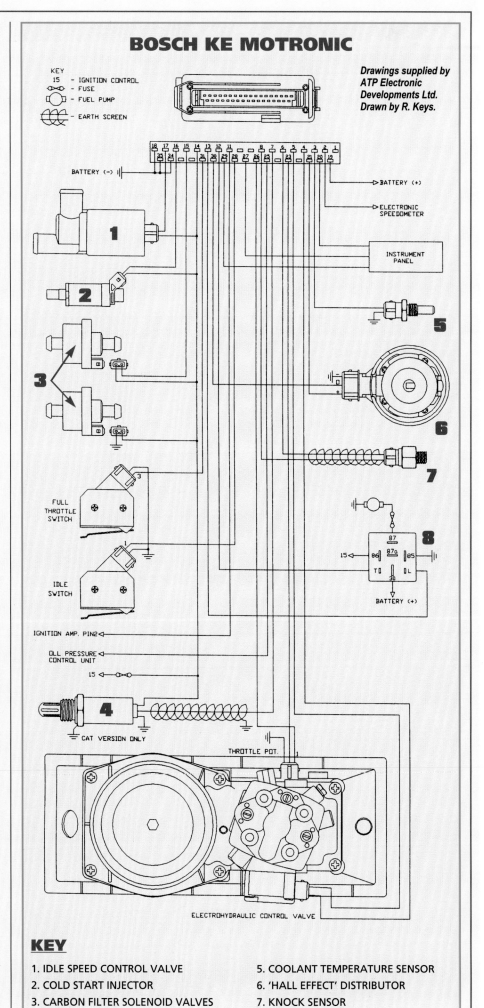

BOSCH KE MOTRONIC

Drawings supplied by ATP Electronic Developments Ltd. Drawn by R. Keys.

KEY
15 – IGNITION CONTROL
– FUSE
– FUEL PUMP
– EARTH SCREEN

BATTERY (–)
BATTERY (+)
ELECTRONIC SPEEDOMETER
INSTRUMENT PANEL

FULL THROTTLE SWITCH
IDLE SWITCH
IGNITION AMP, PIN2
OIL PRESSURE CONTROL UNIT
15
CAT VERSION ONLY
THROTTLE POT.
BATTERY (+)
ELECTROHYDRAULIC CONTROL VALVE

KEY

1. IDLE SPEED CONTROL VALVE
2. COLD START INJECTOR
3. CARBON FILTER SOLENOID VALVES
4. LAMBDA SENSOR
5. COOLANT TEMPERATURE SENSOR
6. 'HALL EFFECT' DISTRIBUTOR
7. KNOCK SENSOR
8. MAIN/FUEL PUMP RELAY

ELECTRONIC DIAGNOSTICS!

How to trace faults in electronic engine management systems

Number 26: Ford's single point EEC-IV KAM management system used on Fiestas and Escorts has developed a poor reputation for drivability problems. Chris Graham discovers the common faults and outlines their practical solutions.

Really the system is not as bad a people make out. Frank Massey, proprietor of Preston-based Fuel Injection Services (Tel: 01772 201597) and our expert guide throughout this series, is not a particular fan of single-point systems but admits that with correct setting this one can work pretty well.

Found on Fiesta and Escort models from the late 1980s and early 1990s,

TYPICAL FAULTS

1. **Drivability problems**
2. **Lack of power**
3. **Poor starting**

Car kindly supplied by:
Stanways of Lytham, Preston Road, Lytham, Lancs. FY8 5BG.
Tel: 01253 794700

Ford denote the system as CFi. The car featured here is an Escort 1.3 but Frank says that the electronic component layout and function is very similar to 1.4-litre Ford applications so this feature is relevant to both

Underbonnet layout is straightforward with good access all round. Most of the important components are located on top of the engine so tuning/repair operations should never be awkward.

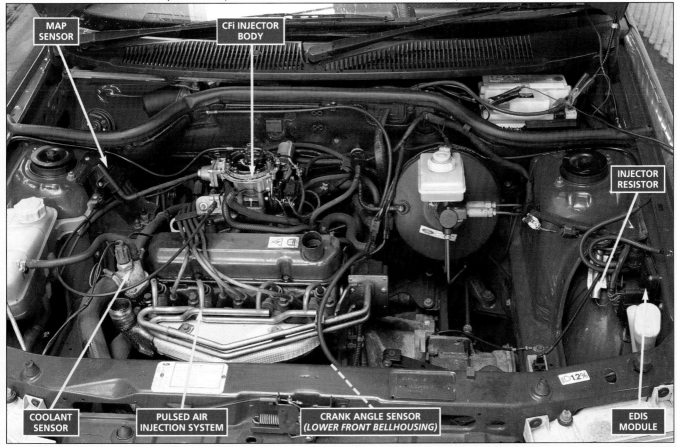

MAP SENSOR

CFi INJECTOR BODY

INJECTOR RESISTOR

COOLANT SENSOR

PULSED AIR INJECTION SYSTEM

CRANK ANGLE SENSOR *(LOWER FRONT BELLHOUSING)*

EDIS MODULE

ENGINE MANAGEMENT

This system provides full engine management (fuelling and ignition control) operated by a 60-pin ECU (in common with all EEC-IV systems) mounted in the left-hand A-post.

A centrally-mounted throttle assembly body houses the injector, a fuel pressure regulator, an idle control motor (DC, plunge type), a throttle position sensor (potentiometer) and an air temperature sensor.

Elsewhere other important system components include a coolant sensor fitted into either the water jacket or the thermostat housing (dependent on application); a MAP sensor (manifold absolute pressure) found on the bulkhead or inner wing; an oxygen sensor mounted in the exhaust downpipe; a crank angle sensor and an EDIS module – in effect an 'intelligent' ignition amplifier which converts the AC crank angle sensor output signals into digital ones and uses these to switch the coil.

In addition there is a ballast resistor in the injector's control circuit, a carbon canister with control solenoid (usually found on the left-hand front wing), a couple of relays (for the fuel pump and ECU power-up), an inertia switch which cuts the pump's power feed in the event of a crash and an octane socket for altering the ignition map to suit different fuel (unleaded or super unleaded). The engine is set to run on 'super' as standard.

The version featured here exhibits a pulsed-air exhaust gas recirculation (EGR) system. This pumps fresh air into the exhaust pipe during warm up to prevent the oxygen sensor from sending a 'go lean' signal to the ECU. The closed-loop (with catalytic converter) exhaust system has to be fooled in this way to prevent the mixture being leaned off too much before the engine has warmed sufficiently.

A code reader socket provides access to stored fault codes but little else of any practical value. The drawback to this Ford system is that there is no warning lamp on the dash so faults can exist without the driver being aware. Fortunately the code system is reasonably comprehensive and accurate.

The system also features 'keep-alive memory' (KAM). In effect there are two fault code registers in the system – one which stores current faults and KAM which stores intermittent faults permanently, assuming battery feed to ECU pin 1 is not lost. If the battery is disconnected KAM is wiped out.

Some components can be driven using the code reader (carbon canister solenoid, idle control motor), but this ability varies with application. It's not a very efficient system according to Frank, so is best regarded as 'code read only'. You can trigger the service mode (code 60) but usually there is no ignition timing or mixture adjustment possible so there is little point in bothering.

When all is well engine performance is OK but not brilliant. The system can suffer with a number of characteristic faults, most of which are interrelated. Putting them right effectively requires a thorough appreciation of how each tuning aspect relates to the other, which is where many garages fall down. Lack of full understanding is a major factor contributing to the car's dubious reputation. Most problems relate to fuelling and many cars will be found running lean and with flat performance.

Preparation

Probably the most essential aspect of preparation with this system is to remove and clean the fuel injector. Most problems afflicting it will relate to the injector itself so its condition is a fundamental. It must be cleaned ultrasonically – the use of in-tank fuel cleaning products can do some good but will rarely clear any established deposits.

All vacuum lines should be checked for signs of swelling or oil/fuel contamination, particularly those relating to the MAP sensor. The use of EDIS ignition means there is no rotor arm or distributor cap to worry about, two HT leads run directly from the coil to each plug.

In most cases the standard leads should be OK but in neglected cases dirt build-up can cause trouble. On CVH engines the plug apertures are deeper so dirt and debris can be collected here. Oil can be a problem here too so wash out thoroughly – upper engine oil leaks are quite common.

The coil pack tends not to give trouble – it usually stays pretty clean. The crank angle sensor can suffer with clutch dust build-up but is easily removed for cleaning. This is usually

worth checking, particularly if the car is suffering with starting problems.

The cleanliness of the air induction system is important too. Some problems can relate to poor breathing and/or oil contamination so check and replace pipes where necessary.

The interlinked nature of many of the problems, particularly drivability ones, which can afflict this engine/management combination mean that sound diagnostics are required to put them right. Straightforward and systematic component replacement (an increasingly common dealer practice these days) will often solve little.

Frank says that Ford are well aware of the drivability problems associated with this set up – official documentation has been produced covering the faults and their suggested solutions. Unfortunately, the list of parts recommended for replacement can result in frighteningly expensive bills (up to £1,000!).

Often suggested by dealers is the replacement of ECUs, gaskets, breathers,

MAP sensors, EDIS modules, etc. All can be faulty but the danger is one of overkill. It is possible for a garage to be panicked into changing the lot, sometimes unnecessarily, so be warned.

Frank's experience is that most problems can be rectified without the need for new parts at all. The cost amounts to little more than a labour charge for the tuning involved.

Typical drivability problems include poor power response. The engine may be 'flat' when the throttle is snapped open for immediate acceleration, or alternatively, there may be hesitation or jerkiness when the throttle is opened after periods of overrun.

To overcome all of this Frank adopts a basic tuning approach which he follows as a matter of routine. He starts by checking the throttle position sensor (potentiometer).

If its signal output is found to be out of specification then improvisation is needed because the component itself is not adjustable. The solution is to carefully bend the control arm (normally

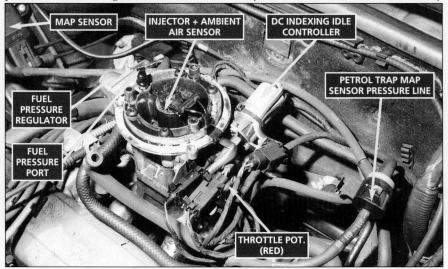

ELECTRONIC DIAGNOSTICS!

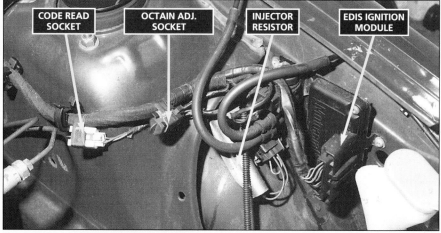

CODE READ SOCKET · OCTAIN ADJ. SOCKET · INJECTOR RESISTOR · EDIS IGNITION MODULE

no more than about 3mm) to achieve the correct voltage output. Ideally this should be set at 0.5-0.7V with the throttle closed.

Commonly Frank finds this output tends to be nearer one volt, which has a detrimental effect on tickover. Idle control is achieved with a reversible DC motor – the voltage is switched to push out and pull in the plunger. This component can become confused by incorrect voltage from the throttle potentiometer, or a sticking injector, leading to erratic idle.

Any re-setting needed must be done off the car and is largely a matter of trial and error if you are inexperienced. Make a series of very slight adjustments and refit and check output after each one.

During this setting procedure it is vital that the idle control motor should be fully disengaged (plunger completely retracted). To achieve this switch on the ignition, open the throttle by hand and push the plunger fully into the body with your finger, then unplug its supply socket to isolate the motor. This will ensure that the throttle closes fully against its stop.

To set the base idle speed (with engine at normal working temperature) the throttle stop may require adjustment. Found on the right of the injector body assembly, this screw may have a hexagonal head or a slotted one.

You must establish whether or not the engine will idle without the influence of the idle control motor. If it will not then adjust the stop accordingly so

that revs are stabilised at about 825rpm. The obvious aim is to set the throttle so that if, during driving, you release the accelerator and the plunger on the control motor retracts fully, the engine will not stall.

With the correct potentiometer voltage and base idle speed set, plug the idle control motor back in and this will then automatically range back to its correct position.

Finally, when dealing with fuelling problems, don't forget to check the MAP sensor. This provides a crucial input to the ECU. Its switch is a digital one and must be electronically clean with a good earth pull down. Any problems with this will cause poor drivability, ranging from hesitation to rich mixture.

A general lack of power is also a common problem on this application and, in many ways, is interlinked with the drivability problems discussed earlier. However there are some useful additional checks to be made if you have a car suffering from poor performance.

First of all remember that the presence of an electronic fault might be sufficient to throw the system into 'code

60', which is when base ignition timing will be set automatically. There is no adjustment potential for ignition timing but it can be checked. If you find that the figure is fixed (no advancing taking place) the chances are that there is a fault to be corrected – this must be identified with a code reader.

If this is not the case then other possibilities include the oxygen sensor. The most common cause of trouble with this component is a slow switching action. The engine may also be running too lean due to carbon build up on the injectors or slightly reduced fuel pressure.

Check the pressure with a gauge – very low on a single-point system like this, about 1.1 bar. Check also the switching of the oxygen sensor. It is vital that this switch extends fully across a range of 0.2-0.8V (ie, an amplitude greater than 0.5V), and that the frequency of this switch is greater than one hertz with the engine at cruise. Ideally it should be two to three hertz.

Problems with the switching can be twofold – either the amplitude or the frequency will be inadequate. Slow switching will create obvious engine surging while incorrect amplitude will

TECHNICAL SPECIFICATIONS

Injector duration	hot	2.5Ms
	cold	4Ms
	cranking	8-12Ms
Map sensor	Idle 18-20in hg	110Hz } Slightly modified
	Atmosphere	160Hz } frequency units available.
Coolant sensor	hot	0.5-1V
	cold	3.5V
Crank angle sensor	cranking	2.5V peak to peak
	idle	5V
Throttle pot.	closed	0.5-0.7V
	open	4.5V
Ambient air	3V approx.	
Main power supplies	pins 37 + 57 ± 0.5V of battery	
Main Earths	pins 20-40-60 0.25V drop or better	
O₂ sensor	200MV-800MV @ 1Hz or better (faster)	
Ignition timing	Base 10-14° BTDC	
Fuel pressure	1.1 bar	
Fuel flow	60 litres/hr +	

THE SERIES SO FAR

No.1	Basic systems – **July 1994**
No.2	Diagnostic equipment – **August 1994**
No.3	Test preparation – **September 1994**
No.4	Ford 2.0i – **October 1994**
No.5	Rover 200/400 – **November 1994**
No.6	Vauxhall 2.0i – **December 1994**
No.7	Peugeot 205/309 GTi – **January 1995**
No.8	Ford 2.9i V6 – **February 1995**
No.9	BMW 1.8i – **March 1995**
No.10	Vauxhall 2.0i 16v – **April 1995**
No.11	Rover 2.0i 16v – **May 1995**
No.12	Rover 1.6/2.0 EFi – **June 1995**
No.13	Rover 1.6/2.0 ignition – **July 1995**
No.14	Ford Zeta 16v – **August 1995**
No.15	VW 1.8 Digifant – **September 1995**
No.16	Honda Legend/Rover 800 – **October 1995**
No.17	Ford XR2i/RS Turbo – **November 1995**
No.18	Peugeot 405 Mi16 – **December 1995**
No.19	Renault Clio 1.2i – **January 1996**
No.20	Vauxhall 24v – **February 1996**
No.21	Range Rover V8 – **March 1996**
No.22	Honda Civic 1.6 – **April 1996**
No.23	Rover 820 single point – **May 1996**
No.24	Jaguar 3.6 straight six – **June 1996**
No.25	Audi 80 – **July 1996**

increase the bias towards the 'go rich' or 'go lean' signal, depending on the voltage level. In this case Frank says that commonly the oxygen sensor will be switching around the 0.2V mark and generating a 'go rich' signal (see Fig.1).

There is no mixture adjustment available but a problem like this can be tackled by tweaking the fuel pressure. On the back of the pressure regulator there is an adjustable stop covered with a plastic cap. This can be altered, in conjunction with a gauge, to increase the fuel pressure very slightly to about 1.2-1.3 bar. This should be sufficient to restore correct sensor switching. Going higher will hinder fuel economy.

If you cannot achieve a satisfactory switch (as observed on an oscilloscope) by altering fuel pressure then the problem is probably with the sensor itself, rather than with fuelling.

Bare in mind that the earth on the oxygen sensor is critical too, because the voltage being switched is small. Before finally deciding to swap the sensor, check the earth value. The voltage drop to earth should be 0.2V or better (lower value). Remember that this component has to switch down to 0.2V so if the earth value is 0.3V the component will never switch properly.

If the earth is not correct then Frank's advice is to wire it directly to battery earth. Don't rely on the existing wiring but lay a supplementary wire and bring it down as low as possible.

Air leaks are another potential cause of trouble with oxygen sensor switching. Keep an eye on exhaust downpipe gasket condition (ahead of sensor), and check any other possible sources of leaking air. Any inlet problem should show up on a manifold vacuum check. A good value of about 450-500mm Hg (18-20in Hg) should be expected, anything less and there is a

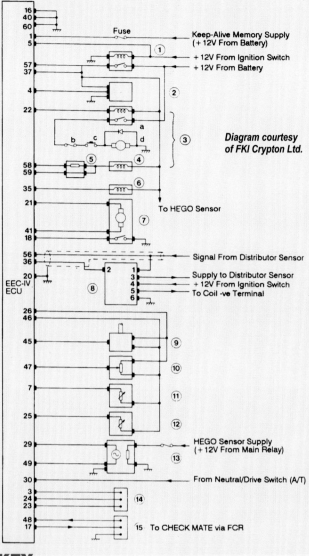

FORD EEC-IV WITH KAM

Fuse
16
40
60
1
5 — Keep-Alive Memory Supply (+ 12V From Battery)
① — + 12V From Ignition Switch
57
37 — + 12V From Battery
4
②
22
③
58
59 — ⑤ ④
35 — ⑥
21 — To HEGO Sensor
41
18 — ⑦
56
36 — Signal From Distributor Sensor
20 — Supply to Distributor Sensor
EEC-IV
ECU — + 12V From Ignition Switch
⑧ — To Coil -ve Terminal
26
46
45 — ⑨
47 — ⑩
7 — ⑪
25 — ⑫
29 — HEGO Sensor Supply (+ 12V From Main Relay)
49 — ⑬
30 — From Neutral/Drive Switch (A/T)
3
24
23 — ⑭
48
17 — 15 To CHECK MATE via FCR

Diagram courtesy of FKI Crypton Ltd.

KEY

1. Main Relay
2. Road Speed Sensor
3. Fuel Pump Circuit
   (a) Relay
   (b) Fuse
   (c) Inertia Switch
   (d) Pump and Diode
4. Injector
5. Resistor
6. Canister Purge Solenoid
7. Throttle Control Motor
8. Ignition Module
9. Manifold Absolute Pressure (MAP) Sensor
10. Throttle Potentiometer
11. Engine Coolant Temperature Sensor
12. Inlet Air Temperature Sensor
13. Heated Exhaust Gas Oxygen (HEGO) Sensor
14. Service Connector
15. Diagnostic Connector

problem somewhere in the system.

Experiencing difficulty when starting the engine is a common fault on these cars and there are a number of potential causes. The first relates to poor output from the crank angle sensor. An AC waveform is produced by the CAS and the minimum voltage required is 2.5V under cranking conditions.

Problems arise when this output level drops to a point when the ECU fails to recognise it. This can be caused because the residual magnetism in the pick-up deteriorates with age – the sensor, although encased in plastic, is mounted in the cast iron block which has an eventual draining effect.

If the output is found to be low then the first option is to remove and clean the component. If this makes no difference then consider the positioning of the sensor. If it is too far from the flywheel the inductive effect will be reduced and output lowered. Closing this gap may be achieved with a replacement unit (about £15) but if not then either the sensor body or the casting will have to be altered very slightly.

A further possibility is that the EDIS module is at fault. There is a chance that it may be being electronically spiked under cranking. Ford have produced an updated version which may be worth trying. Older units have a part number prefixed by '89' while the improved versions show '91'. Replacements cost about £100.

To conclude then, this system can be tricky and expensive to deal with for the unwary. Be mindful that hefty bills are a possibility if you entrust the work to a main dealer or anyone else who is unable to think on his feet.

For training courses – specialist to novice, system or equipment-based – ring Frank on 01772 201597.

NEXT MONTH
Vauxhall
Astra/Cavalier
1.8 OHC.

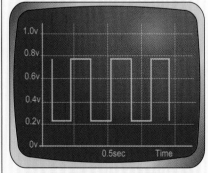

This trace represents a good oxygen sensor output signal. Amplitude is greater than 0.5V and the switching rate is excellent.

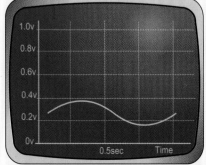

This trace shows a slow switch with insufficient amplitude. Being around the 0.2V mark will be triggering a permanent 'go rich' signal.

Fig. 1

ELECTRONIC DIAGNOSTICS!

How to trace faults in electronic engine management systems

Number 27: Although simple and generally reliable, the 'stand alone' Bosch LE3 fuel injection system fitted to many Vauxhall 1.8i applications has several significant weaknesses. Chris Graham checks them out.

Much favoured by vehicle manufacturers in the late 1980s, the Bosch LE3 fuel injection system provided a simple and cost-effective way of bringing an engine up-to-date during the development transition between carburettors and full blown engine management.

Used on Vauxhall Nova (GTE), Astra, Belmont, Cavalier and Carlton

TYPICAL FAULTS
1. **Low speed drivability**
2. **Engine non-start**
3. **Poor cold starting**

1.8i applications, the system first appeared in 1986. It represented a progression from the previous LE2 system with the big difference being that a

much smaller ECU was located directly on top of the airflow meter.

Frank Massey, the electronics guru behind Preston-based Fuel Injection Services (Tel: 01772 201597) is a fan of this approach, explaining that it simplifies the system by reducing the amount of wiring.

Bosch LE3 normally works in conjunction with a modular-based or programmed ignition system. In the case

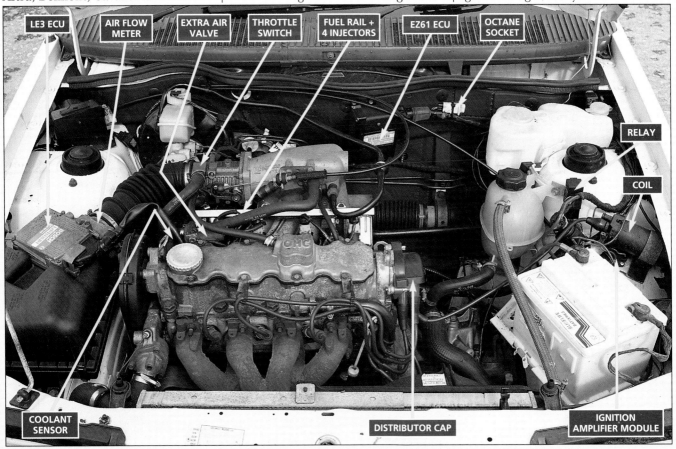

LE3 ECU — AIR FLOW METER — EXTRA AIR VALVE — THROTTLE SWITCH — FUEL RAIL + 4 INJECTORS — EZ61 ECU — OCTANE SOCKET — RELAY — COIL — COOLANT SENSOR — DISTRIBUTOR CAP — IGNITION AMPLIFIER MODULE

ENGINE MANAGEMENT

The LE3 fuel injection system is certainly one of the simpler examples around. It is a multipoint set-up running through four conventional fuel injectors. All are triggered together by a single output from the main ECU.

The number of major components involved is small and consists of an airflow meter (vane type); a conventional throttle body; an adjustable throttle switch; an auxiliary or extra air valve; a coolant temperature sensor (in water jacket near thermostat); a fuel pressure regulator; a dual action main relay (controlling ECU and fuel pump/extra air valve power-up) plus an externally-mounted fuel pump and filter.

The extra air valve is a simple thermal device which provides basic yet very effective idle control. The throttle switch has idle and full-load contacts only – again simple and reliable. Operating it by hand (don't rely on throttle linkage) will produce an audible click as soon as the throttle is opened but there is nothing to be heard at the top end, although a set of points are closed at the 'full load' position.

The earth 'pull down' for the main relay is via the ECU for safety reasons – it cuts the pump if the engine stops during an accident. The main trigger for the LE3 system is supplied by the EZ61 ignition ECU. This black box is mounted in the centre of the bulkhead at the rear of the engine bay. Consequently, defects with the ignition system lead directly to problems on the fuel side.

Timing is not adjustable as such but there is an octane socket – one of two fuel ratings can be selected. There is no fault code reading potential on this LE3 system at all, not even a flashing warning light on the dashboard to flag up a problem. The only indication of trouble will come from 'real life' drivability problems or complete engine failure.

---

of the MkII Astra featured here it links to the Bosch EZ61 control system which has its own separate ECU, rather than a module by the coil.

Frank says the big advantage of LE3 is its simplicity. The wiring loom is normally entirely separate from the rest of the vehicle and all accessible from under the bonnet.

The whole system is generally pretty reliable – the short wiring runs and direct four-pin connection between ECU and airflow meter are big factors in this respect. The ECU itself is smaller than most, with just 15 pins which again reduce the likelihood of trouble. Nevertheless, there are characteristic weaknesses, often relating to vehicle age and/or poor maintenance.

Preparation

Although this system is inherently reliable, given the passing of time and the fact that as standard LE3 was pretty 'tight' on fuelling (an early effort at 'lean burn'), there can be problems related to lean running.

The extra air valve does not normally cause problems. It contains a simple bi-metallic strip-operated slotted disc which allows more air to pass when the engine is cold. The bleed gradually shuts as the engine warms.

Frank has never known one to fail but says it is worth checking anyway. Inspect for blockages and damage to the rubber piping to and from. The valve cannot be stripped but effective cleaning can be achieved either with an aerosol product or ultrasonically.

The quality and speed of engine idle can and will deteriorate if the throttle body becomes dirty so, as part of basic preparation, wash this out carefully and make sure the throttle stop has not been adjusted. If it has been moved then it will need to be re-set. To do this back it off until the throttle disc fouls the body and then advance it until it just starts to lift clear, then lock it in that position.

After setting the stop, check the operation of the throttle switch. The audible click should occur immediately the throttle starts to open. Make sure also that it clicks every time that the throttle is released – no pressure should be required when closing.

Frank's advice when checking this is never to rely entirely on the click as an indicator of correct operation. He has experience of switches which have become disconnected inside so that although the click takes place, no changes in voltage output are initiated. Use a multimeter or oscilloscope to check electrical performance to be completely sure.

There is no mixture adjustment on the air flow meter itself, this is accomplished via a potentiometer on the ECU. A nylon-headed screw provides about 20 turns stop-to-stop and this adjustment actually alters injector duration. Going beyond this limit will not cause damage but takes the pot. out of specification. When this happens each turn of the screw is marked by a quiet click – normally you will need to listen down the screwdriver or use a stethoscope to hear this.

Frank's approach to setting the pot. is to wind it to the end of its adjustment (either way) until you hear the first click, and then to wind back ten revolutions. This will ensure a middle setting. The intention (as with any potentiometer like this) is that it should be used for minor trimming adjustments.

If you have to move it significantly from the mid-range position then there is certainly something else wrong. Factors such as fuel pressure, injector condition and coolant sensor performance should all be considered.

The ignition side of this management package is vital so check everything carefully. Make sure that the distributor cap and rotor beneath are clean and dry. The cap was covered as standard with a black plastic protector. These often serve to collect dirt and moisture behind and can be troublesome. Frank advises throwing them away altogether.

Check the plug apertures for dirt, the leads for good condition and the plugs themselves for the correct specification.

Common complaints

We've already mentioned that the LE3 system tends to err on the lean side with regard to fuel mixture and, in later life, this can lead to problems. Factors such as a deterioration in injector performance, carbon build-up on the valves, induction air leaks and poor HT performance can all be at the

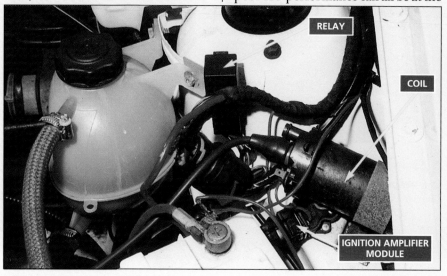

ELECTRONIC DIAGNOSTICS!

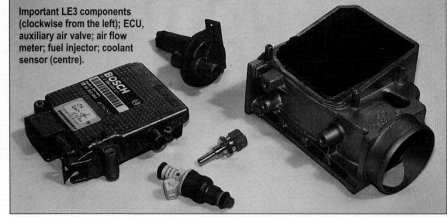

Important LE3 components (clockwise from the left); ECU, auxiliary air valve; air flow meter; fuel injector; coolant sensor (centre).

root of significant drivability problems.

Such a complaint will usually be most noticeable at low speeds during initial throttle take up. This will include both starting from stationary and high-speed cruising when light throttle is being used. There will be general hesitation and a lack of response.

The induction hose between the ECU/air flow meter and the engine is a rubber bellows-type affair which is prone to age-related splitting. Such damage may not be obvious during a casual inspection so check it specifically. Remove and stretch it out to inspect condition carefully.

A common occurrence is that engine movement during acceleration causes splits to open up (creating a horrible flat spot in performance) and then close again when the vehicle stops – an easy fault to miss if the pipe is not removed for a thorough inspection. Replacements cost about £18.

Bear in mind also that these Vauxhall engines have a reputation for drawing in manifold gaskets. Have a listen around the inlet manifold to make sure the seal is good. If in doubt replace it because leaks here are a disaster from a tuning point of view.

So assuming there is nothing obviously wrong, your first efforts to correct engine hesitation should be directed at the basic settings. Confirm that the throttle switch is working properly and adjusted correctly (two mounting screws in slotted holes). If you are happy that the disc itself is correctly set then check switch operation with reference to audible click and a meter.

If you find that all is well with the basic tuning set-up (including the HT side) and the problem still persists, then Frank's advice is to check the injectors. Removal and ultrasonic cleaning is the sure-fire way to get things right. The vital factors are spray pattern and delivery rate. Tolerances with these are pretty fine in this case and Frank says that anything more than 10% out of spec will lead to problems.

Judging this performance is a matter of experience. It is impossible to quote actual figures because professional flow benches vary from machine to machine. For this reason you should seek out an experienced specialist who will recognise and appreciate what he sees.

Most injectors will have been in place for up to 10 years now and Frank believes that only a minority will have ever been cleaned properly. Removal is not difficult and if they are dirty then cleaning will bring instant results. Fuel economy and general drivability will be improved at a stroke.

Another cause of hesitation can be a problem with the bearings within the airflow meter. If you have established that all is well with basic set-up, the injectors and the ignition side then consider this as a likely cause.

The bearings can dry out with age which means that the response of the air vane is inhibited and becomes sluggish. The consequence of this is that mixture enrichment will not occur as quickly as it should, leading to drivability problems.

The bad news is that although this is a relatively simple mechanical problem, there is little which can be done to put it right apart from fitting a replacement unit. Access to the bearing assembly for lubrication is restricted so

TECHNICAL SPECIFICATIONS

Throttle switch	Pin 2 closed – 0V
	            open – 5V
	Pin 3 closed – 0V
	            open – 5V
	Pin 18 – Earth

Coolant sensor	Supply – 5V Earth – 0.25V Hot – 0.5-1.0V Cold – 2.0-2.5V Default – 3.5V
Injector duration	Hot – 2.5ms Cold – 3.5-4.0ms Cranking – 2.5ms hot, 4.0-6.0ms cold

Air flow meter	Pin A – Air temp, 2.0-3.0V at 20°C
	Pin D – Supply 5V
	Pin C – Earth 0.25V
	Pin B – Output – Ign. on – 0.2-0.3V
	                          Idle – 0.75-1.0V
	                          3,000rpm – 2.00-2.5V
	                          Open throttle – 4.5V (min)

Fuel flow rate	80lt/hr
Fuel pressure	Vacuum – 2.0-2.2 bar No vacuum – 2.3-2.7 bar
ECU trigger	Pin 1 – 5V digital from ignition (speed signal)
Auxilliary air valve	12V permanent supply (residual heat supplied from block)

THE SERIES SO FAR

No.1	Basic systems –	**July 1994**
No.2	Diagnostic equipment –	**August 1994**
No.3	Test preparation –	**September 1994**
No.4	Ford 2.0i –	**October 1994**
No.5	Rover 200/400 –	**November 1994**
No.6	Vauxhall 2.0i –	**December 1994**
No.7	Peugeot 205/309 GTi –	**January 1995**
No.8	Ford 2.9i V6 –	**February 1995**
No.9	BMW 1.8i –	**March 1995**
No.10	Vauxhall 2.0i 16v –	**April 1995**
No.11	Rover 2.0i 16v –	**May 1995**
No.12	Rover 1.6/2.0 EFi –	**June 1995**
No.13	Rover 1.6/2.0 ignition –	**July 1995**
No.14	Ford Zeta 16v –	**August 1995**
No.15	VW 1.8 Digifant –	**September 1995**
No.16	Honda Legend/Rover 800 –	**October 1995**
No.17	Ford XR2i/RS Turbo –	**November 1995**
No.18	Peugeot 405 Mi16 –	**December 1995**
No.19	Renault Clio 1.2i –	**January 1996**
No.20	Vauxhall 24v –	**February 1996**
No.21	Range Rover V8 –	**March 1996**
No.22	Honda Civic 1.6 –	**April 1996**
No.23	Rover 820 single point –	**May 1996**
No.24	Jaguar 3.6 straight six –	**June 1996**
No.25	Audi 80 –	**July 1996**
No.26	Ford Escort/Fiesta –	**August 1996**

a long-term solution is impossible. Re-furbished (with warranty) and new air-flow meters are available for about £100 and £200 respectively.

Frank adds that some technicians opt to re-value the spring tension within the air flow meter in a bid to overcome the bearing problem. He is not keen on this approach because, apart from the fact that it is easily damaged, he says it will not cure the bearing problem completely and will tend to lead to over-fuelling elsewhere in the rev range – not a professional solution.

The second common fault with this system is complete engine failure. When this occurs you may well find all is well on the ignition side – good trigger signal being sent to the LE3 ECU – but there will be no injection taking place or fuel pump operation.

Inside the LE3 ECU the section on the left (light grey panel) as viewed here is all 'surface-mounted' components. Nobody can repair this sort of technology at present.

The most usual cause of this is an internal problem within the ECU itself. It is failing to 'pull down' the main relay which, in turn, prevents the fuel pump from running. The bad news is that there is no cure for this fault other than a replacement ECU.

Unfortunately, Frank is not aware of any specialist currently repairing this type of ECU. The problem is that the internal components are 'surface mounted' on to the board and replacements are simply not available. The only alternative for genuine ECU faults is a replacement unit.

In such instances prepare yourself for a £300 bill. The short-cut solution is to rewire the relay so that it has a permanent earth and a switched supply. However, the danger with this is that it bypasses the safety feature of the standard system – the pump will not be cut if the engine stops in the event of a crash, unless you wire an inertia cut-out switch in as well. The sort which unlock central-locking systems will do and may

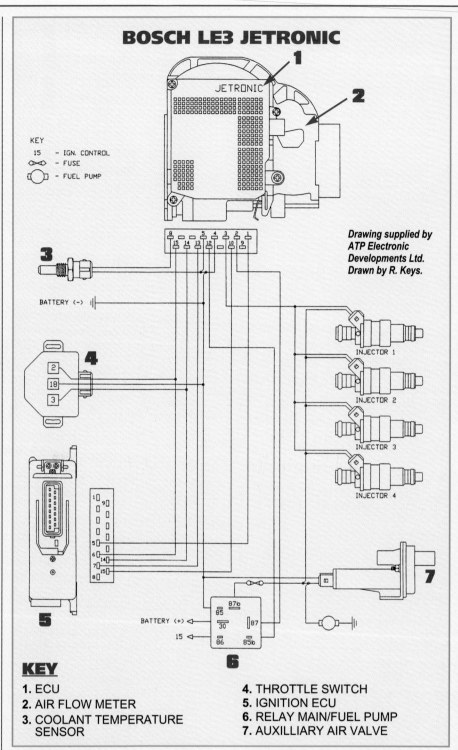

BOSCH LE3 JETRONIC

Drawing supplied by ATP Electronic Developments Ltd. Drawn by R. Keys.

KEY
15 – IGN. CONTROL
– FUSE
– FUEL PUMP

BATTERY (-)

INJECTOR 1
INJECTOR 2
INJECTOR 3
INJECTOR 4

BATTERY (+)
15

KEY

1. ECU
2. AIR FLOW METER
3. COOLANT TEMPERATURE SENSOR
4. THROTTLE SWITCH
5. IGNITION ECU
6. RELAY MAIN/FUEL PUMP
7. AUXILLIARY AIR VALVE

be found on appropriate cars in breakers' yards. Essentially though, Frank does not recommend this 'solution'.

Finally, problems can be experienced with the coolant sensor and present themselves in the form of poor cold starting. While the engine will eventually start, performance while it warms will be noticeably poor.

The sensor is an NTC type (voltage starts high when cold and reduces as it warms) with a 5V supply. Conventionally the output when cold will be about 3.5V, dropping to about 1.0-0.5V when hot. In this case, however, there is an exception to the rule. An internal resistor within the LE3 ECU lowers output voltage when cold to 2.0-2.5V – as measured at ECU pin 8.

Confusion can arise because if the sensor fails it will default to a 3.5V output which can be interpreted as being fine for a cold engine when the actual reason is sensor failure. The only solution is to fit a replacement which costs about £15 for the genuine Bosch component.

NEXT MONTH
Saab 900/9000.

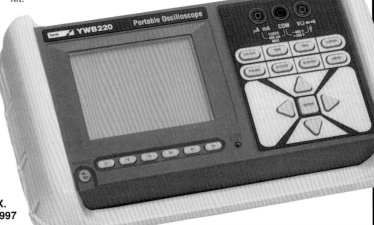

ELECTRONIC DIAGNOSTICS!

How to trace faults in electronic engine management systems

Number 28:
The Bosch LH engine management system used by Saab on non-turbo 900 and 9000 models is essentially reliable but when trouble strikes it can be expensive. Chris Graham reports.

Saab chose to split the engine control on its 900 and 9000 16v models. From the mid-1980s separate Bosch systems managed fuelling and ignition and, while both were stand-alone, there were important links between the two.

On these non-turbo models fuelling is controlled by a Bosch LH set-up, in the case of the K-reg 9000i featured here, in 2.4 guise. This is a well tried

system used on many other popular vehicles. Ignition is provided by a Bosch EZ arrangement. It is fully mapped and makes use of a signal generator within the distributor (Hall effect generator) on early models, a crank angle sensor more recently.

According to Frank Massey, proprietor of automotive electronics experts Fuel Injection Services (Tel: 01772 201597) the Saab installation is gener-

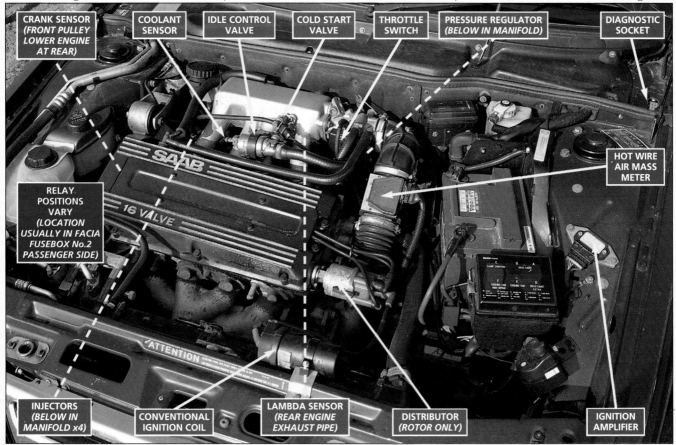

CRANK SENSOR *(FRONT PULLEY LOWER ENGINE AT REAR)*
COOLANT SENSOR
IDLE CONTROL VALVE
COLD START VALVE
THROTTLE SWITCH
PRESSURE REGULATOR *(BELOW IN MANIFOLD)*
DIAGNOSTIC SOCKET
HOT WIRE AIR MASS METER
RELAY POSITIONS VARY *(LOCATION USUALLY IN FACIA FUSEBOX No.2 PASSENGER SIDE)*
INJECTORS *(BELOW IN MANIFOLD x4)*
CONVENTIONAL IGNITION COIL
LAMBDA SENSOR *(REAR ENGINE EXHAUST PIPE)*
DISTRIBUTOR *(ROTOR ONLY)*
IGNITION AMPLIFIER

ENGINE MANAGEMENT

Bosch LH is a hot-wire system based around an air mass meter. On late models a catalyst was fitted making the fuelling side totally closed-loop – no mixture adjustments possible.

The EZ ignition system features a separate module/amplifier which makes spark-related diagnostics relatively straightforward. A trigger signal runs into this module, is converted to a square wave and is then sent to switch the coil. In addition a signal is also sent to pin 1 of the main LH ECU, providing the trigger for the fuel injectors. This additional trigger is crucial and should always be checked first with any potential fuelling problem.

Fuelling is controlled from the three basic ECU inputs – engine speed (pin 1 on LH ECU, from EZ unit), load and temperature. The hot wire in the air mass meter creates a variable voltage output relative to the induction air passing it. In this way engine load is measured.

On non-cat models the air mass meter will have an adjustment potentiometer screw for trimming the mixture – no such facility exists on cat-equipped versions which are controlled by a Lambda sensor.

Other important components in the management system include: a two-wire NTC coolant sensor; a throttle switch; a rotary idle control valve; a pair of control relays (main and fuel pump) and four fuel injectors.

Fuel supply is conventional but sometimes there are two pumps – priming and main. If there are two both are controlled by the same fuse pump relay.

The system works on intermittent injection – all injectors are triggered together, twice per cycle. The basic fuelling curve is calculated from the coolant sensor mounted in the water jacket at the back of the cylinder head just below the inlet manifold – normally with a blue plastic connector socket.

A standard fuel rail supplies the injectors, with a control regulator on the return side to maintain correct pressure. The rotary idle control valve is a digital unit which is controlled directly by the LH ECU. There is a limited amount of idle speed adjustment via the throttle disc but essentially this should be ECU-governed.

There is a dedicated diagnostic socket under the bonnet – n/s bulkhead under a black plastic cover – but Frank says this is of limited value to the DIY owner. Its one practical function is checking the ignition trigger (measured at pin 5 on this socket).

The main ECU is mounted either under the scuttle, near the wiper motor, or beneath the front passenger seat, depending on the year of manufacture. Under the driver's seat there are two diagnostic sockets on later models but these provide access to fault codes only, no serial communication is possible.

Regrettably there is little potential for code reader toting enthusiasts because, as far as Frank is aware, the software required is simply not available on the aftermarket.

ally well engineered under the bonnet. There are few weak spots where water or dirt cause problems and the engine bay tends to remain clean.

The system essentially is a reliable one. Fuelling is efficient – injectors hardly ever need cleaning – and serious problems, bearing in mind the marque's relatively low volumes in the UK, are few and far between.

Preparation

The good news is that very little preparatory work is normally required on these Saab models.

A cosmetic steel cover secured by four bolts sits on top of the cylinder head hiding the plugs and leads. Remove the plugs, check their gaps and replace as necessary. Check the condition of the HT leads although these are well routed and tend not to suffer with heat or contamination.

Wash the distributor cap, check the condition of the rotor arm and remove the air induction hose to gain access to the throttle body. Check and wash the disc as necessary.

There are a couple of rubber hoses which run to the rocker cover – one large and one small. Frank advises that both can suffer from oil impregnation so check for spongy consistency or cracking. Air leaks in any vacuum hoses will cause running problems.

Check the ignition module which is fairly exposed on the n/s inner wing. It can suffer with water ingress, as can the air mass meter.

It is important also to check the setting of the throttle stop and the oper-ation of the throttle switch. If you are suspicious about stop tampering then follow this method for re-setting. Back it off completely so that the disc shuts totally. Slacken off the switch too because this can interfere with disc travel. Then slowly advance the stop until the disc just lifts off the body, lock it up and set the switch at this position.

To assess switch operation use a voltmeter at ECU pin 2. You need to make sure the voltage output is changing correctly. It should switch from zero volts with the throttle closed, to 12V as soon as it opens. This reading should remain across the range until the full load setting is reached, when the signal should switch back to zero again.

Frank warns that working on this engine requires plenty of 'deep' work around the inlet manifold. Access can be limited so working with a cool engine will help avoid too many burns etc.

A breakout box used between the

Saab's dedicated diagnostic socket on nearside bulkhead. Pin 5 can be probed to check presence of ignition trigger.

ECU and the harness, or back-probing the main ECU socket, provides a more convenient approach.

One of the most common problems with this engine management application is ignition failure – usually related to the ignition module (amplifier). In the worst case when the engine will not run check the basics first. Make sure of the spark and if this is non-existent then test the coil for a ground switch (dwell angle). Should this be absent then progress back to pin 1 on the Bosch LH ECU (or pin 5 on under-bonnet diagnostic socket) and test for the main ignition trigger originating from the EZ module.

Pin 1 at the ECU will really have to be checked using an oscilloscope because the trigger signal is a square wave. A dwell or multimeter could be used (switched to 'frequency') but this will not identify the quality of the signal – the vital factor.

Frequency varies with engine speed so is inconsequential. The shape of the switch must be assessed. Its consistency, allied to good supply and ground characteristics ('sharply' square) are the crucial factors only discernible from a scope screen. Frank says that, commonly, problems lie with the module but emphasises that before condemning it you must make sure it has a 12V supply, a good earth and is receiving the trigger (from pin 16 on EZ ignition ECU).

Erratic or non-existent coil switching are terminal problems for the module. No repairs are possible so a new unit will be needed. Genuine replacements from Bosch cost about £120 according to Frank. Other

ELECTRONIC DIAGNOSTICS!

makes are available for considerably less but quality is reduced.

A good diagnostic rule of thumb is that this type of ignition fault causing misfires usually becomes worse with speed. This is in contrast to mechanical faults (poor valve seating, injector defects etc.) which tend to get better with speed.

Problems with fuel mixture, either too rich or too lean, are also relatively common on this application. Often, Frank says, this can be attributed to a poor quality signal from the air mass meter. The symptoms are hesitation and generally poor drivability.

The air mass meter generates a variable voltage output determined by the cooling effect of the induction air on a heated wire. When viewed on a scope ideally the signal should be a clean line with no visible interference or 'noise' accompanying it.

Output can be measured on a meter but the problem is that this will be an averaged reading. Potentially vital small variations in output quality (as little as 0.25V) can be sufficient to

The air mass meter's main socket can suffer with water ingress. Corrosion in here will corrupt its vital output signal.

upset fuelling but remain completely invisible to a meter which averages them out.

Frank says that the fine tolerance on this signal makes it hard for anything other than a scope to be a practical detection device. Most diagnostic tools, including code readers, will not even sniff it.

A tell-tale sign of this condition is a car which runs badly for 20 seconds or so after starting but suddenly then becomes smoother. Essentially what is happening is that the ECU is detecting a fault with the air mass meter and throwing the system into default or

'limp home' mode. Once this happens the engine will run better at idle but be lean at all other times with noticeably flat performance.

The air mass meter contains its own hybrid circuitry on top of the unit and internal, age-related faults with this can be at the root of the problem. Once again, before condemning the unit check its supply (socket can suffer with water ingress) and earth values. Remember also that signal interference could be coming from another external source – an alternator or starter motor etc.

Internal faults with the air mass meter can only be tackled by replacement. New ones cost about £350 so be sure that the fault is genuinely with the unit before taking the plunge.

The third and final typical fault is a potentially misleading one found on later cars. It manifests itself as an overfuelling problem but, in fact, relates to the distributor. On these applications there is no timing control within the distributor, just a rotor arm. Unfortunately, not everyone appreciates this and Frank has had cases where the distributor body has been rotated in a misguided attempt to adjust timing.

TECHNICAL SPECIFICATIONS

Diagnostic socket **(under bonnet)**	Pin 1 Battery Pin 2 Ground Pin 3 Crank feed Pin 4 Ignition feed Pin 5 Trigger to LH pin 1
Bosch EZ ignition ECU	Pin 17 – trigger out to Bosch LH ECU pin 1 (digital, square wave, 12V amplitude) Pin 16 – Trigger output to amplifier (digital, square wave, 12V amplitude)
Throttle switch	Pin 2 – 0V closed, 12V open Pin 18 – Ground Pin 3 – 12V open, 0V closed
Coolant sensor	Open circuit – 4.5V Cold – 3.5V Hot – 0.5V
Idle control valve	Supply – 12V from main relay Output – digital switch, 12V amplitude at 100Hz (ECU pin 33)
Lambda sensor	Output – 200-800Mv at 1-5Hz (ECU pin 24) Heater supply fused from pin 87on pump relay
Fuel injectors	Duration, hot – 2.2-2.5ms, cold – 3-4ms

Air mass meter	Pin 1 – Ground
	Pin 3 – Output Static – 1.5V
	                         Idle – 2.5V
	                         Cruise – 3V
	Pin 4 – Burn off 4 secs after switch
	                         off. Pulse approx.
	                         4-5V for 1ms
	Pin 5 – Supply from main relay (pin 87B)
	Pin 6 – Potentiometer (non-cat models)

Main relay	Pull down ECU pin 21
Fuel pump relay	Pull down ECU pin 20

The coolant sensor (blue socket viewed here from above) is tucked away awkwardly at the back of the engine under the manifold.

THE SERIES SO FAR

No.1   Basic systems – **July 1994**
No.2   Diagnostic equipment – **August 1994**
No.3   Test preparation – **September 1994**
No.4   Ford 2.0i – **October 1994**
No.5   Rover 200/400 – **November 1994**
No.6   Vauxhall 2.0i – **December 1994**
No.7   Peugeot 205/309 GTi – **January 1995**
No.8   Ford 2.9i V6 – **February 1995**
No.9   BMW 1.8i – **March 1995**
No.10 Vauxhall 2.0i 16v – **April 1995**
No.11 Rover 2.0i 16v – **May 1995**
No.12 Rover 1.6/2.0 EFi – **June 1995**
No.13 Rover 1.6/2.0 ignition – **July 1995**
No.14 Ford Zeta 16v – **August 1995**
No.15 VW 1.8 Digifant – **September 1995**
No.16 Honda Legend/Rover 800 – **October 1995**
No.17 Ford XR2i/RS Turbo – **November 1995**
No.18 Peugeot 405 Mi16 – **December 1995**
No.19 Renault Clio 1.2i – **January 1996**
No.20 Vauxhall 24v – **February 1996**
No.21 Range Rover V8 – **March 1996**
No.22 Honda Civic 1.6 – **April 1996**
No.23 Rover 820 single point – **May 1996**
No.24 Jaguar 3.6 straight six – **June 1996**
No.25 Audi 80 – **July 1996**
No.26 Ford Escort/Fiesta – **August 1996**
No.27 Vauxhall 1.8i – **September 1996**

All this achieves is to alter the air gap between the tip of the rotor arm and the segments in the cap. When set correctly this gap is at its minimum so any movement away from the ideal will widen it. The consequence of this is that more electrical energy is consumed in straddling the enlarged gap and so spark duration at the plug is shortened.

Because there is less spark but the same amount of fuel the car will run rich, or at least appear to do so. A gas analyser will diagnose the problem as a fuelling fault so it is easy to be fooled into chasing off down this route looking for the cause.

What should be the giveaway is the plug firing voltage. This will be increased because the energy required to fire is greater but burn time or spark duration will decrease. This should normally be significantly over one millisecond but if the air gap is increased even slightly then duration can drop back close to one millisecond (on all four plugs).

This is a significant reduction but is nevertheless sometimes overlooked by inexperienced technicians. It will send HC emissions rocketing leading to the conclusion that either the mixture must be leaned off or, on later cars with a cat, there is a problem with the Lambda sensor switching.

To set the air gap correctly is simple. Make sure the plugs are clean and correctly gapped, and then, while watching the plug firing voltages, rotate the distributor until the reading drops to the lowest value. This will correspond to the smallest rotor-to-segment gap which is as it should be.

NEXT MONTH
VW Golf GTi MkII.

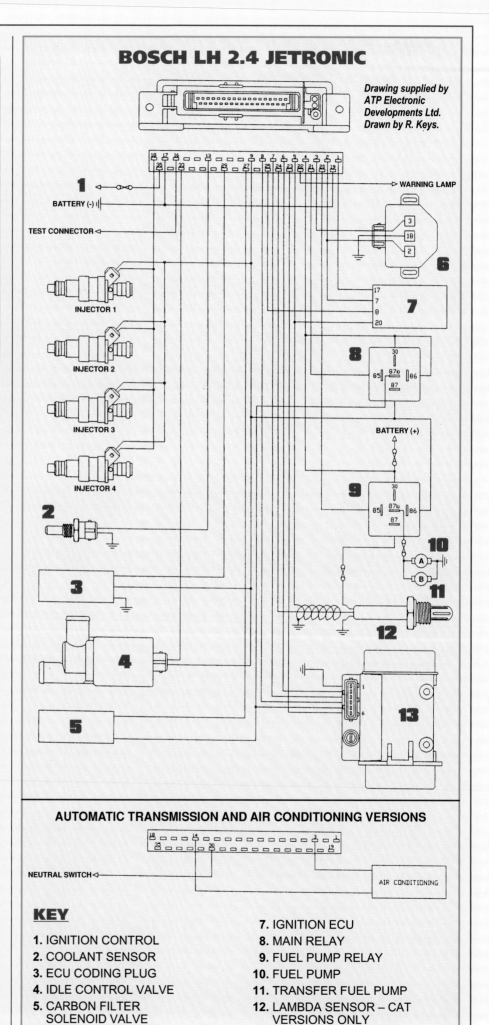

BOSCH LH 2.4 JETRONIC

Drawing supplied by ATP Electronic Developments Ltd. Drawn by R. Keys.

WARNING LAMP
BATTERY (-)
TEST CONNECTOR
INJECTOR 1
INJECTOR 2
INJECTOR 3
INJECTOR 4
BATTERY (+)

AUTOMATIC TRANSMISSION AND AIR CONDITIONING VERSIONS

NEUTRAL SWITCH
AIR CONDITIONING

KEY

1. IGNITION CONTROL
2. COOLANT SENSOR
3. ECU CODING PLUG
4. IDLE CONTROL VALVE
5. CARBON FILTER SOLENOID VALVE
6. THROTTLE SWITCH
7. IGNITION ECU
8. MAIN RELAY
9. FUEL PUMP RELAY
10. FUEL PUMP
11. TRANSFER FUEL PUMP
12. LAMBDA SENSOR – CAT VERSIONS ONLY
13. AIR MASS METER

ELECTRONIC DIAGNOSTICS!

How to trace faults in electronic engine management systems

Number 29: *We return to the ever popular Golf with a further look at the VAG Digifant system as used on the MkII GTi. Chris Graham investigates.*

Volkswagen Golfs are renowned for their build quality and general durability. The GTi models invariably lead a life of merciless thrashing and yet, in most cases, they can take it.

Electrics and engines are generally strong but do have their characteristic weaknesses. We first looked at this system way back in episode number 15 (*CM* Sept. 1995 issue) so reference should be made to that feature to back up all

TYPICAL FAULTS
1. **ECU failure**
2. **Unstable idle**
3. **Poor starting**

the new information included here.

Frank Massey, proprietor of Preston-based Fuel Injection Services (Tel: 01772 201597) says that Digifant first arrived in 1988 on Golf GTi ap-

plications and continued until 1991. It normally works well but its downfall can be wiring related. Frank is starting to see more failures caused by wiring problems now and so this episode concentrates primarily on these.

Overall the Digifant engine management system is straightforward to work on. Most of the techniques required are basic and there should be little requirement for expensive diagnostic equipment.

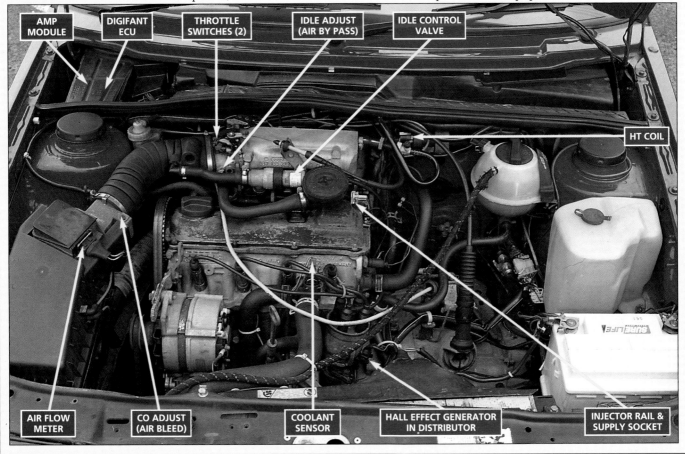

AMP MODULE · DIGIFANT ECU · THROTTLE SWITCHES (2) · IDLE ADJUST (AIR BY PASS) · IDLE CONTROL VALVE · HT COIL · AIR FLOW METER · CO ADJUST (AIR BLEED) · COOLANT SENSOR · HALL EFFECT GENERATOR IN DISTRIBUTOR · INJECTOR RAIL & SUPPLY SOCKET

ENGINE MANAGEMENT

Digifant uses a Hall effect trigger which is quite unusual for engine management systems – most utilise an AC signal generator on the crankshaft to produce the all important system trigger.

The Hall effect unit, located within the distributor, generates a square-wave signal which is sent to the ECU. From this the coil drive or dwell value is calculated and used to trigger the fuel injectors.

The injectors are straightforward solenoid-operated components. All are triggered together from the same output (ECU pin 12) so it is intermittent injection with each injector being fired twice per four-stroke cycle.

The system also incorporates a knock sensing circuit to detect pinking and then retard the ignition as necessary. This works very effectively according to Frank. Because of its efficiency it allowed the software engineers to advance engine timing as aggressively as possible. They did this safe in the knowledge that any pinking problems would be managed by the knock sensing system. The result is crisp, responsive engine performance across the range.

The ignition system itself is fairly conventional with a rotor arm in the distributor, a traditional cap and conventional plug leads. There is an ignition amplifier which is mounted next to or on top of the 25-pin ECU – found next to rear bulkhead on o/s of vehicle. The combination is protected by a flimsy plastic cover and while this may appear vulnerable, Frank says he has never seen an ECU suffering from water ingress.

The engine management system make up is pretty standard. Its operation is dependent upon the three basic inputs – engine speed, load and temperature. Speed is determined by the Hall effect distributor. The load signal comes from a dated but efficient air flow meter sited on the main induction system. A 'door' within the unit is deflected by the induction air and the degree of opening induces a change in voltage output which is interpreted by the ECU as a load signal.

Within the air flow meter there is the facility for basic CO adjustment via an air bleed screw. Frank says that the Bosch air flow meters on this application are extremely reliable. He has never changed one so be wary if you are advised to do so.

Temperature input comes from a coolant temperature sensor mounted in the thermostat housing. This is a two-wire NTC component so its voltage output starts high and then drops as temperature increases.

There are two throttle switches fitted. The presence of twin throttle butterflies, with a mechanical cam arrangement which progressively opens the second one, dictates that separate idle and full load switches are required. Both are two-wire microswitches, the idle one being mounted on top of the throttle body and the full load one underneath. Hand operation will produce an audible click.

Engine idling performance is controlled by a two-wire rotary idle control valve which is driven directly by the ECU. However, good idle performance is determined by correct basic idle set up. For this the management system has to be switched into a service mode to disarm the valve. We covered this in detail last time so refer back if you need reminding.

The system uses two relays – the main one switches on the ECU when the ignition key is turned, while the second one is brought into play when the engine is cranked and activates the fuel pumps.

Also of note is that here are two fuel pumps – one, for priming, is in the tank and the main one is external. The correct operation of both is vital.

There is no prospect for the use of serial communicators and a fault code facility is absent on this age of vehicle too (it did come with later models). Even dash-mounted warning lights are omitted so the only indicator of faults is via the car's performance.

Preparation

Because most of the trouble is likely to be electrical in nature, your basic preparation should start with the distributor cap. It will normally be fitted with a metal RF shield and this can be responsible for collecting dirt and debris. Clean it out thoroughly.

Remove the cap and check inside. Frank says that VWs of this age tend to suffer with unwanted deposits in here and these must be dealt with. Washing should be carried out using a good degreasing agent followed by an air line to blow it dry. If the cap is excessively grubby then replace it with a good quality new component.

The HT leads can also be at the root of trouble. Although they are of good quality as standard and the leads themselves rarely cause problems, the ends can do. Part of the trouble is caused by the siting of the coil. Found on the bulkhead this component attracts dirt, moisture and general grime. Corrosion often results if the unit is not kept clean and this can work its way into the lead connections.

Disconnect and inspect all of them and clean up as necessary. Pay attention to the coil body as well. A very real danger here is that excessive corrosion build up can lead to electrical energy escaping back to the ECU or module via the king lead. It feeds back through the ignition amplifier to pin 1 on the ECU and can cause irreparable internal damage.

At the plug end the leads feature metal shrouds for shielding heat. Once these age they can start to leak electrically. Frank's solution, to save buying a new set of leads, is to re-terminate these with BMW rubberised boots which happen to be an exact fit and last longer.

Frank says that problems on the ignition side other than those mentioned are rare unless the distributor itself has

Distributor contains Hall effect generator. Keep an eye on its connector. It faces forward and is exposed to dirt and moisture. Wiggle it with the engine running and if you can detect any change then there is a problem with dirt ingress.

been badly adjusted.

Always make a point of thoroughly cleaning out the idle control valve and washing the throttle body. Make sure also that both throttle switches are audibly clicking in operation. In some cases the linkage will be fitted with a damper but Frank thinks it best to back this off to let the throttle shut cleanly.

You may also wish to consider professional injector cleaning as part of basic preparation. Frank says that problems in this department are becoming more common now as the MkII GTi ages with many older examples starting to suffer with drivability problems.

Take time to check fuel pump operation too – both of them. It is critical that the pair are working effectively. If the priming pump fails then performance will be very flat at the top end although the engine will keep running. If the main pump fails the engine probably will not run at all.

If during your inspection you detect a noisy main pump then this can be a tell-tale sign that the primer is suffering. The extra loading on the main unit will wear it rapidly.

Finally, if you find that you cannot obtain the correct CO adjustment on the air flow meter then the problem probably lies with the fuel injectors. However, bear in mind fuel pressure as a possible cause too. Carry out fuel pressure and flow checks (to test for air in the fuel which will not be highlighted by a pressure check alone) before jumping to any conclusions.

ELECTRONIC DIAGNOSTICS!

Fault finding

Perhaps the worst potential fault with this system is a complete ECU failure. Frank has come across this a number of times and says that, unfortunately, the causes can be many and varied.

From a diagnostics point of view one of the first checks should be to test the ignition amplifier. If this is to blame then there will be no signal at the coil but the trigger signal at pin 25 of the ECU will be present.

If, on the other hand, the ECU is at fault then the pin 25 trigger signal will be lost because the ECU will be failing to drive the amp. Under these conditions, and assuming that all the other basics are correct and the relays are operating, the two most likely causes are either HT electrical spikes from the distributor cap and/or the coil, or a problem with the main engine earth strap.

In the latter case it can be leaking electrolyte at the root of the problem. The earth strap attaches to the battery tray and if the battery has been leaking corrosion will eventually result. This can partly or totally eat through the strap to prevent its efficient operation. Faced with such an electrical restriction the engine will seek earth through an alternative route, which is when the fun starts.

One convenient option is via the ECU. A number of components have an earth return direct into this crucial component and the upshot can be a heavy electrical load which proves terminal. This can be anything up to

The microswitch on top of the throttle body relates to engine idle control – keep an eye on its connection leads which can become over-tightened due to engine movement.

150A if supplied by the starter motor which, for a component never intended to carry more than 10-15A, spells disaster. Frying tonight!

The only solution is a new ECU – about £120. Remember, if you are faced with this scenario, to seek out the cause. This is vital if an expensive repetition is to be avoided. Frank's advice is that if you are in any in any doubt about the condition of the earth strap then replace it. You may also consider re-locating it away from the battery tray to a convenient point on the engine block, thus preventing further trouble.

Another very common problem with this system is an unstable idle speed. We mentioned in the Passat feature that this often will be caused by nothing more than dirt in the control valve. However, there can also be problems with the throttle microswitch found on top of the throttle body.

A tightness in the wiring harness can interfere or cut completely the supply contact to this switch so check for this carefully. There is quite a lot of engine movement under acceleration on this Golf application, but when the car is stationary everything looks fine – this can be deceptive. All wires tend to work harden with age so fractures are also a possibility in this case.

This sort of failure will prevent the idle control valve from working and it can be locked either shut or open. If the problem is intermittent as the supply quality fluctuates, then intermittent stalling and/or over-revving will result.

Stress test the wiring by manipulating it by hand. If a problem is found then you will have to extend the harness to create more slack.

You may also find unstable idle speed linked to poor starting performance. The possible cause of this prob-

TECHNICAL SPECIFICATIONS

Throttle switch (ECU pin 11)	0.25V at idle and full load 4.5V at any other position	
Air flow meter (ECU pin 17)	5V supply	
Vane output (ECU pin 21)	0.25-0.5V closed 0.8-1.2V at idle	4-4.5V fully open 1.6-2V at 3,000rpm (static)
Idle control valve ECU pin 22)	Switches between 0-10V during cranking or running	
Coolant sensor (ECU pin 10)	1-1.5V cold engine 0.2-0.4V hot engine	
Ambient air sensor (ECU pin 9)	1-2V	
Knock sensor (ECU pin 4)	Voltage output tiny at ECU pin 4 or at sensor itself	
Ignition amplifier	Pin 1 – dwell switch Pin 2 – earth, no more than 0.25V Pin 3 – unused Pin 4 – 12V supply Pin 5 – unused Pin 6 – Engine position signal (digital) from ECU Pin 25, 8V switched to ground	
Hall effect switch	10V square switch to ground, to ECU pin 18 (inside distributor)	
Coil output	30,000-35,000V	
Plug voltages	12,000V at idle 15,000V under load	
Regulator voltage	13.5-14.5V	
Ignition timing	6° at 800rpm (in service mode)	
Fuel pressure	2.5bar at idle, vacuum attached 3bar with vacuum removed	
Fuel flow rate	80 litres/hour	
Injector duration	2.5ms hot 10ms under load enhancement	4-5ms cold
Idle speed	900-1,000rpm (in service mode)	
CO	0.5-1.5% at idle	0.2-0.5% at cruise
HC	100-300ppm at idle	under 100ppm at cruise
CO_2	14% at idle	15% at cruise
O_2	1% at idle	0.5-1% at cruise

THE SERIES SO FAR

No.1   Basic systems – **July 1994**
No.2   Diagnostic equipment – **August 1994**
No.3   Test preparation – **September 1994**
No.4   Ford 2.0i – **October 1994**
No.5   Rover 200/400 – **November 1994**
No.6   Vauxhall 2.0i – **December 1994**
No.7   Peugeot 205/309 GTi – **January 1995**
No.8   Ford 2.9i V6 – **February 1995**
No.9   BMW 1.8i – **March 1995**
No.10 Vauxhall 2.0i 16v – **April 1995**
No.11 Rover 2.0i 16v – **May 1995**
No.12 Rover 1.6/2.0 EFi – **June 1995**
No.13 Rover 1.6/2.0 ignition – **July 1995**
No.14 Ford Zeta 16v – **August 1995**
No.15 VW 1.8 Digifant – **September 1995**
No.16 Honda Legend/Rover 800 – **October 1995**
No.17 Ford XR2i/RS Turbo – **November 1995**
No.18 Peugeot 405 Mi16 – **December 1995**
No.19 Renault Clio 1.2i – **January 1996**
No.20 Vauxhall 24v – **February 1996**
No.21 Range Rover V8 – **March 1996**
No.22 Honda Civic 1.6 – **April 1996**
No.23 Rover 820 single point – **May 1996**
No.24 Jaguar 3.6 straight six – **June 1996**
No.25 Audi 80 – **July 1996**
No.26 Ford Escort/Fiesta – **August 1996**
No.27 Vauxhall 1.8i – **September 1996**
No.28 Saab 900/9000 – **November 1996**

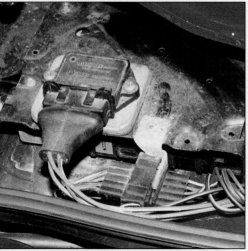

The ECU sits tucked away under the o/s front lip of the bulkhead. It is normally covered with a rigid but flimsy plastic cover which is clipped into place. Water ingress is not usually a problem.

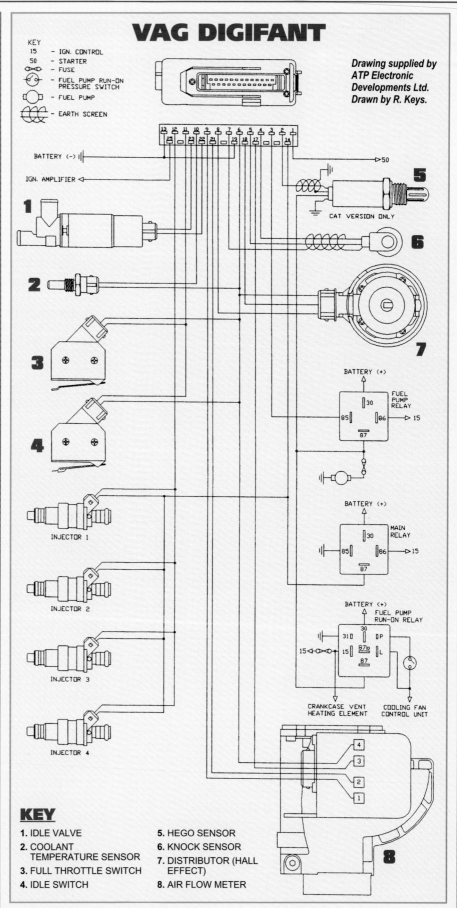

VAG DIGIFANT

Drawing supplied by ATP Electronic Developments Ltd. Drawn by R. Keys.

KEY
15 – IGN. CONTROL
50 – STARTER
– FUSE
– FUEL PUMP RUN-ON PRESSURE SWITCH
– FUEL PUMP
– EARTH SCREEN

KEY

1. IDLE VALVE
2. COOLANT TEMPERATURE SENSOR
3. FULL THROTTLE SWITCH
4. IDLE SWITCH
5. HEGO SENSOR
6. KNOCK SENSOR
7. DISTRIBUTOR (HALL EFFECT)
8. AIR FLOW METER

---

lem is that the fuel injection harness may have become damaged.

The wires to the injectors run at the back of the engine and are over-lapped by an earth strap connecting the rocker cover to the bulkhead at the rear of the engine bay (next to coil bracket). Normally this strap should be bonded to the coil but it can work loose to act upon the injection supply harness.

The danger is that the harness's plastic insulation eventually will be breached and when this happens one of two things will follow, neither of which are pleasant! If the strap happens to rub through on the supply side of the harness there will be a short to the relay which will get extremely hot and blow. This relay is not fused so if it grounds to earth there is the potential for a major wiring fire.

The alternative is for the strap to chafe through the injector earth circuit. This will increase injector triggering and lead to over-fuelling. It can be intermittent in its early stages before the insulation is completely broken down, causing erratic fuelling, rich mixture and poor starting performance.

Consequently, it is well worth spending time inspecting the under-bonnet wiring. Watch for any signs of chafing, loose, broken or missing retaining clips and corrosion.

NEXT MONTH
Cavalier 2-litre SRi.

ELECTRONIC DIAGNOSTICS!

How to trace faults in electronic engine management systems

Number 30: This month we step into the future with a look at Vauxhall's latest Ecotec engine management system to discover what might go wrong in years to come. Chris Graham reports.

Vauxhall call it Ecotec but others refer to GM's newest all-singing, all-dancing engine management package as Simtec. Whichever you choose there is no confusion about the system's abilities.

Frank Massey, the tuning maestro behind Preston-based Fuel Injection Services (Tel: 01772 201597), considers Simtec to be a state-of-the-art system which illustrates perfectly the way technology is progressing. It points to-

POTENTIAL PROBLEMS
1. **Crank angle sensor**
2. **DIS ignition**
3. **Oxygen sensor**

wards a tuning era when very sophisticated test equipment will be a basic requirement.

The version featured here, 56.1 as found on a late 2.0-litre Cavalier SRi, is typical of the breed, possessing sev-

eral interesting technological advances and significantly enhanced processing power from its 55-pin ECU.

Simtec arrived in 1993 and is used across the modern Vauxhall range on 16v applications and succeeds Motronic 2.5, 2.6 and 2.7. There are different versions in use (56.3, 56.5 etc.) and Frank believes the choice between them relates to vehicle specification, in particular the fitment of goodies such as traction control.

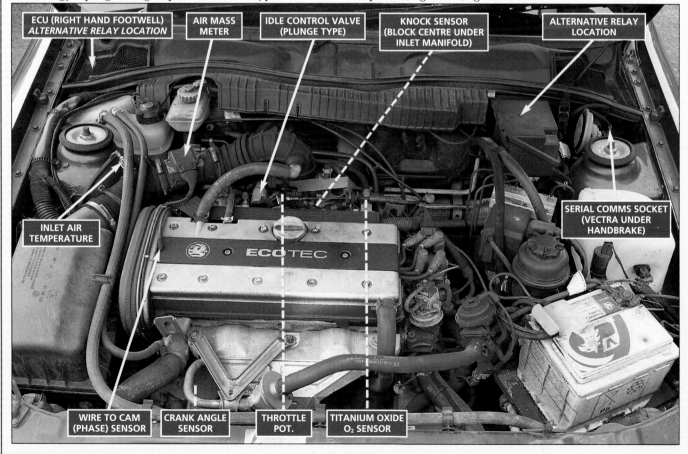

ECU (RIGHT HAND FOOTWELL) *ALTERNATIVE RELAY LOCATION* — AIR MASS METER — IDLE CONTROL VALVE (PLUNGE TYPE) — KNOCK SENSOR (BLOCK CENTRE UNDER INLET MANIFOLD) — ALTERNATIVE RELAY LOCATION — SERIAL COMMS SOCKET (VECTRA UNDER HANDBRAKE) — INLET AIR TEMPERATURE — WIRE TO CAM (PHASE) SENSOR — CRANK ANGLE SENSOR — THROTTLE POT. — TITANIUM OXIDE O₂ SENSOR — ECOTEC

ENGINE MANAGEMENT

The first thing to note about Simtec 56.1 is that anyone familiar with the previous Motronic systems should find plenty of similarities. While there are some significant component differences a lot of the new set-up actually remains much about the same.

At the core of the system is an air mass meter which is virtually identical to the Motronic component – based around a film resistor sensor rather than a wire.

Also, in common with late Motronic systems, there is a throttle position sensor, air and coolant temperature sensors, a knock sensor, an idle control valve (plunge rather than rotary – similar to Ford) and a dual relay – one half powering-up the ECU and the other supplying the fuel pump, under ECU control.

Nevertheless, despite the familiarities, this system does introduce a new range of potential problems as far as the technician is concerned. Primary among these is the exceptionally high speed of some selected sensor outputs.

Successfully monitoring these requires top-spec. diagnostic equipment if worthwhile analysis is to be achieved. Unfortunately Frank says that the motor vehicle, digital scope-based engine analyser is no longer up to the job. Complex and expensive 'live' digital storage 60mhz band width scopes are required to catch the rapid switching and glitches at time intervals in the nano second ranges involved.

It is the crank angle sensor which is likely to cause most problems in this respect. It is completely different from those found on older engines and is a four-wire component instead of three. We'll deal with its intricacies later.

Other points of interest include a camshaft phase sensor which enables the ECU to calculate injector timing, a DIS (distributorless) ignition system with one coil per two cylinders and multipoint fuel injection through four solenoid-operated, two-wire injectors.

The ignition system uses a single coil pack and demands specific diagnostic equipment for tracking trouble effectively. While by no means new – DIS is found on the 2CV! – the system can be confusing and needs to be understood because it is fast becoming the industry standard.

There is a diagnostic socket positioned at the rear, n/s corner of the engine bay on this Cavalier application but which has been moved inside the car, under the handbrake on new Vectra models.

Regrettably, Frank says that currently there is no independently produced software (Vauxhall of course have their dealer-only version) for use on the Simtec system. However, Sykes-Pickavant have a programme at the fully working pre-production stage form which will go on sale in the spring.

Other options which may or may not be fitted, depending upon model, include a pulsed air system (secondary air injection). If this is present you will find a large fan in the engine bay which delivers air into the exhaust system. Ford have been using this arrangement for a few years and the idea is simply to fool the oxygen sensor into thinking that the mixture is leaner than it really is during warm up.

This prevents the sensor from sending the 'go lean' instruction to the ECU too quickly, thus allowing the cold start enrichment to run for a suitably long time. In addition it provides emission advantages as well.

The ECU controls the fan via a relay, basing its decisions on coolant temperature, throttle position and engine speed inputs. The introduction of more air into the exhaust manifold increases the burning of hydrocarbons and so lowers emission levels at the tailpipe. In addition the higher temperature heats the cat more quickly, bringing it rapidly up to operating temperature.

There may also be an exhaust gas recirculation (EGR) system which again is computer controlled. The idea of this is to control the production of toxic nitrogen oxides (NOx), which are most readily produced when the engine is hot.

A small amount of inert exhaust gas is reintroduced back into the inlet manifold to help lower combustion temperature within the cylinders. The action is solenoid controlled and is activated usually at high speed, while the engine is being cruised on the motorway. It does, of course, reduce power.

Obviously EGR and the secondary air injection systems cannot both work at the same time because one would defeat the other. Effective control is therefore essential so it is fortunate that the brains within the Simtec ECU are very powerful.

The power and speed of the computer allows it to react to sudden changes in driving style – for example, it will switch off all emission control the instant hard acceleration is detected.

When this happens the extra fuel needed is ensured because the oxygen sensor is switching in open loop and a function called 'evap control' is activated. The carbon canister which, during normal running, absorbs the fumes from the petrol tank rather than allowing them to vent to the atmosphere, is drained. This reserve provides a useful source of extra fuel which is drawn by vacuum into the engine via an ECU-controlled solenoid valve.

The problem with this system, from this feature's point of view, is that there are no problems! As Frank says, it is still very early days yet in the life of Simtec. Real life problems are few and far between – Frank has not seen any himself – and so far the system is proving utterly reliable.

Being honest Frank does not anticipate many inherent problems but admits that he cannot yet be sure about factors such as wiring quality, routing and component layout. Whether these factors prove to be durable in the long term remains to be seen.

The whole theory behind modern engine management is that gradual component or engine-related deterioration is countered by automatic compensation within the ECU – block learn etc. However, the reality is not so comfortingly simple and, Frank's experience suggests that such refinements do not really work – cars still go 'flat' with age.

The other downside, from a driver's point of view, is that progressive development of engine management systems, while making engines more efficient, reduces overall performance. For example, the original Astra 16v was a bullet on wheels with a tremendously flexible engine providing sparkling performance. Frank considers that, by comparison, the latest Astra GSi 16v, while still not a slow car, lacks the zest and excitement of the original.

Preparation

Preparation should pose few problems with this system. There is no distributor cap to worry about but take time to check each plug lead for cuts or other damage. These are routed under an engine cover so careless fitting can trap them, often resulting in misfires and electrical shorting.

It's worth noting that misfires on this type of engine will often be hard to detect. If there is a short occurring from lead to head, and the voltage demand for this is about the same as the plug would normally demand, the problem is electronically invisible. Common sense has to take over.

Thankfully, the ignition system is relatively simple. There are no moving parts so no maintenance requirements with caps or rotors etc. Nevertheless, make sure the plug apertures are clean and specify good quality plugs – do not compromise. Many of these engines are now being specified with platinum plugs because of the load demand on them and this should be followed.

While these may seem expensive – about twice as much as copper plugs –

Frank says they will last for 40-60,000 miles which is at least three times the mileage potential of normal ones and they give better performance too.

The idle control valve is always worth a look. It has the potential to cause engine hesitation or surging so remove it, wash out with carburettor cleaner and replace. Check and clean the throttle intake as well removing any oil residue or other carbon contamination you may find.

This engine has a total closed-loop emission control system so there is no mixture adjustment potential at all. Basic tuning is therefore a matter of confirming that the primary components, such as the oxygen sensor, are switching correctly and that the injectors are in good, serviceable condition.

Also make sure the air cleaner is clear and that all vacuum hoses are unobstructed, tightly secured and free from damage. The style of control on this engine means that any air leaks will cause real problems.

Potential problem areas

As we've already stressed, no established problems have surfaced yet with the Simtec system. However, there is scope for confusion in several key areas for those not familiar with the set-up.

ELECTRONIC DIAGNOSTICS!

The first component to be aware of is the crank angle sensor. This switches rapidly so assessing its quality of performance with anything other than a top-spec oscilloscope very difficult.

However, Frank says that it is possible to observe part of its waveform using a motor vehicle scope set on a very short time base – two milliseconds or so. Nevertheless, you must be aware that because this component switches at about 4,000Hz (that's 4,000 times a second!) at idle, anything you 'capture' will be just a tiny proportion.

One practical way to capture the signal and make it easier to look at is to remove the plugs from the engine and crank it over on the starter. This reduces the engine speed from 900 to about 300rpm so more of the signal will be visible. Alternatively, the engine can be turned even more slowly by hand. The amplitude of the signal should be about two volts peak-to-peak.

Of course, spinning the motor manually, or with the plugs removed, will simply establish the quality of the signal but will tell you nothing of its output frequency. Unfortunately, most common faults with crank angle sensors tend to be heat and vibration-in-

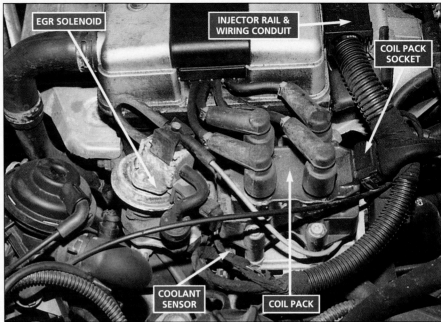

EGR SOLENOID | INJECTOR RAIL & WIRING CONDUIT | COIL PACK SOCKET | COOLANT SENSOR | COIL PACK

duced – only occurring when the engine is running at high revs. Consequently, this sort of defect will not show if the motor is being turned slowly.

Fortunately, the crank angle sensor is well covered in the comprehensive range of fault codes provided by the Simtec management system. Frank says that in most cases you will be able to rely on the accuracy of these to do the diagnostic leg work for you in the absence of an adequate scope.

The DIS or wasted spark ignition system on this engine is not new but is worth detailing here. In this case cylin-

ders one and four are paired together, as are two and three. When the coil is induced each end discharges, one positive and the other negative, to one pair of plugs. Both ends fire at the same time but one coincides with compression while the other fires during the exhaust stroke – hence the name 'wasted spark'.

The coil is actually being fired half as quickly as a conventional unit which gives it longer to charge up thus creating the potential for a greater energy output. On the down side the spark plugs take a hammering because they are firing at twice the normal frequency although in practice this should not be a problem assuming good ones are fitted.

The plug which is fired by the positive end of the coil always shows a slightly higher operating voltage than the negative one. Don't be fooled by this into re-gapping in an effort to correct the apparent imbalance because this is how it should be. The difference will normally be 5-6kV.

With regard to examining the ignition system you will not need dedicated DIS equipment unless you want to do cylinder balance or spark kill tests. Looking at the low tension control circuits is straightforward but you have to consider each circuit in its own right. If you have equipment which is programmable then select 'four stroke, two cylinder'. Each half of the engine should be regarded as a separate two-cylinder unit and then factors like dwell, coil charge time and plug burn times will all be correct and measurable.

The other component which has changed dramatically is on this new system is the oxygen sensor. The component is a four-wire unit and switches between five volts and ground. Older (zirconium dioxide-based) sensors cre-

TECHNICAL SPECIFICATIONS

NTC coolant sensor	3.5V @ 20°C 1.4V @ 85°C
Air temperature sensor	1.8V @ 20°C 1.5V @ 85°C
Lambda sensor	5V to 0V @ 2-3Hz with hot engine at 3,000rpm
Throttle potentiometer	0.5V closed 4.5V with throttle fully open (smooth transition between the two)
Air mass meter	0.5V at idle (hot) 1.2V approx. at cruise 3.75V snap throttle
Knock sensor	AC waveform, approx. 2V peak to peak
Idle control valve	12V to ground
Crank angle sensor	AC waveform, 2V peak to peak (by hand, no plugs in engine)
Fuel injectors	3.2ms at 900rpm (hot) 3.0ms at 3,000rpm (hot) 10ms during cold cranking (System is sequential, ie. one pulse per 720°)

THE SERIES SO FAR

No.1   Basic systems – **July 1994**
No.2   Diagnostic equipment – **August 1994**
No.3   Test preparation – **September 1994**
No.4   Ford 2.0i – **October 1994**
No.5   Rover 200/400 – **November 1994**
No.6   Vauxhall 2.0i – **December 1994**
No.7   Peugeot 205/309 GTi – **January 1995**
No.8   Ford 2.9i V6 – **February 1995**
No.9   BMW 1.8i – **March 1995**
No.10   Vauxhall 2.0i 16v – **April 1995**
No.11   Rover 2.0i 16v – **May 1995**
No.12   Rover 1.6/2.0 EFi – **June 1995**
No.13   Rover 1.6/2.0 ignition – **July 1995**
No.14   Ford Zeta 16v – **August 1995**
No.15   VW 1.8 Digifant – **September 1995**
No.16   Honda Legend/Rover 800 – **October 1995**
No.17   Ford XR2i/RS Turbo – **November 1995**
No.18   Peugeot 405 Mi16 – **December 1995**
No.19   Renault Clio 1.2i – **January 1996**
No.20   Vauxhall 24v – **February 1996**
No.21   Range Rover V8 – **March 1996**
No.22   Honda Civic 1.6 – **April 1996**
No.23   Rover 820 single point – **May 1996**
No.24   Jaguar 3.6 straight six – **June 1996**
No.25   Audi 80 – **July 1996**
No.26   Ford Escort/Fiesta – **August 1996**
No.27   Vauxhall 1.8i – **September 1996**
No.28   Saab 900/9000 – **November 1996**
No.29   VW Digifant update – **December 1996**

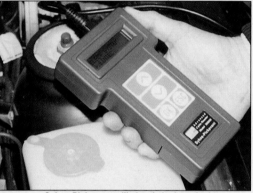

Sykes-Pickavant will shortly be introducing software for use on Simtec 56.1 via their Code Reader. Call 01253 721291 for details

ated a tiny voltage when an oxygen differential was detected, switching between zero and one volt in the process. No supply voltage was required.

The modern versions, as in this case, are titanium oxide-based. They do not produce a voltage in their own right and need a supply to operate. In this case the oxygen sensor relies upon a five-volt feed from the ECU and its resistance changes as variation in oxygen concentration is detected – a true sensor. It is able to respond very rapidly to variations in oxygen content and so works extremely efficiently.

Finally, it should be noted that one of the other wires from this sensor carries a digital signal which Frank understands is an internal diagnostic function for the ECU. He thinks it is used to enable the ECU to monitor rapidly the performance of the sensor.

NEXT MONTH
Nissan Micra 16v.

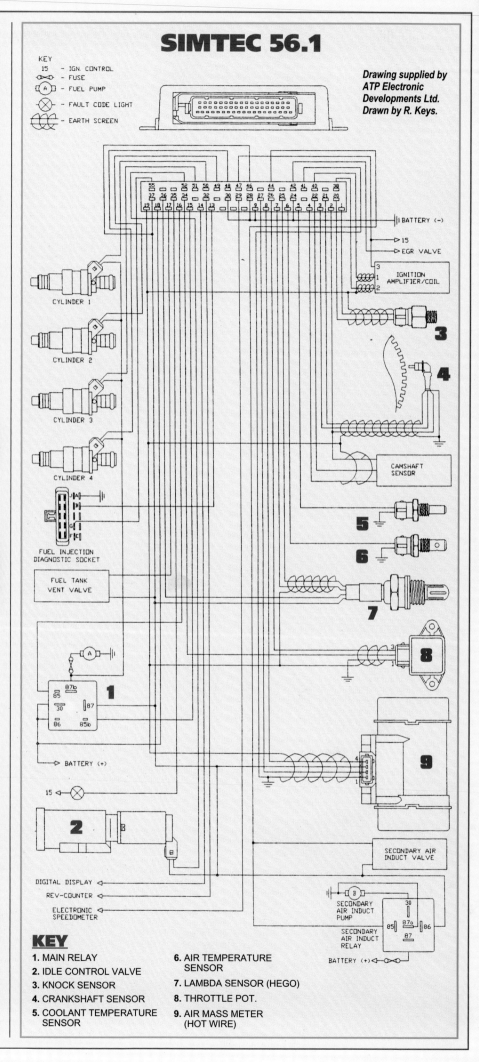

SIMTEC 56.1

Drawing supplied by ATP Electronic Developments Ltd. Drawn by R. Keys.

KEY
15 – IGN. CONTROL
– FUSE
A – FUEL PUMP
– FAULT CODE LIGHT
– EARTH SCREEN

KEY

1. MAIN RELAY
2. IDLE CONTROL VALVE
3. KNOCK SENSOR
4. CRANKSHAFT SENSOR
5. COOLANT TEMPERATURE SENSOR
6. AIR TEMPERATURE SENSOR
7. LAMBDA SENSOR (HEGO)
8. THROTTLE POT.
9. AIR MASS METER (HOT WIRE)

ELECTRONIC DIAGNOSTICS!

How to trace faults in electronic engine management systems

Number 31: Chris Graham investigates the inner workings of Nissan's popular 'bubble' car, the new 16v Micra.

The new Nissan Micra, with its friendly, cheerful appearance, has been with us since 1992. The car is available with either 1.0 or 1.3-litre 16v engines which are managed by Nissan's own ECCS system.

According to Frank Massey, our independent electronics expert and training specialist (Call Fuel Injection Services on 01772 201597 for details), both engines are pretty advanced for a car in this sector of the market. The

POTENTIAL PROBLEMS
1. **Misfires**
2. **Poor economy**
3. **Throttle pot.**

Car kindly supplied by:
Pat Kelly at Sykes-Pickavant

fact that the ECU is a thumping 113-pin component is testament to that.

To date, however, this relative complexity is not posing many problems.

The system is coping well with the rigours of the UK climate and serious problems have yet to surface. What follows is a description of the basic system, its workings and a few potential trouble spots for the future.

Preparation and problems

Most Japanese engines tend to run 'clean' in terms of dirt and oil deposits in the engine bay. These units are no exception. Frank puts much of this down

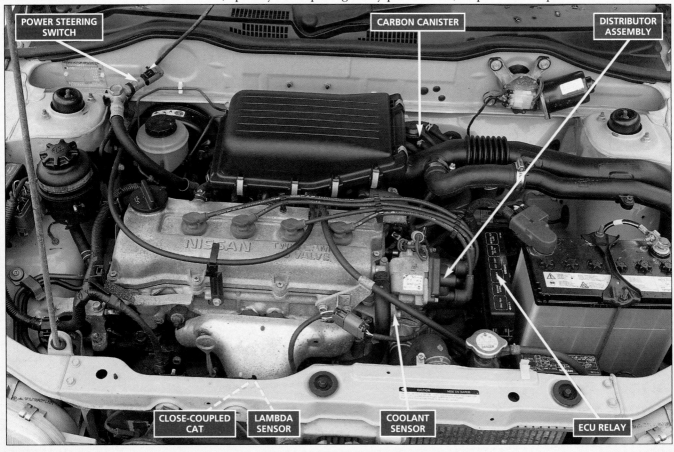

POWER STEERING SWITCH

CARBON CANISTER

DISTRIBUTOR ASSEMBLY

CLOSE-COUPLED CAT

LAMBDA SENSOR

COOLANT SENSOR

ECU RELAY

ENGINE MANAGEMENT

Both these 16v engines have total engine management provided by Nissan's own ECCS package. A single ECU – found under the dash – regulates ignition and fuelling profiles, with inputs from sensors around the engine.

Essentially the system runs on multi-point injection with one injector per cylinder. While a good thing, this approach rather flies in the face current European thinking, Frank says. At the small car end of the market here the trend is towards single-point fuel injection with all the inherent drivability problems which go with it.

Frank is not a fan of single-point and believes the Japanese have been wise to maintain multipoint technology right across their engine ranges. In addition, the Micra's fuel injection is sequential – again pretty advanced stuff for a small car. Each injector is triggered specifically to the firing sequence, acting rather like a spark plug, to deliver the shot of fuel precisely when required.

On the ignition side of things what appears to be a standard-looking distributor is, in fact, not. The coil and ignition amplifier are both integral within the distributor, together with vital engine position and speed sensors. A composite trigger signal emerges from here and is sent to the ECU which, in turn, calculates injector timing.

To investigate the performance of the coil, using a standard engine analyser, requires a custom-made metal sleeve which fits snugly over the distributor cap and acts as an 'aerial' to pick up the RF output from the coil. You could make one of these but its fit must be exact. Any air gaps between the sleeve and the outside of the distributor will distort the readings being taken.

To access true coil signals remove the cap, attach a fly lead to the winding, replace the cap and then test. The impor-tant trigger signals can be monitored from a five-pin socket at the side of the distributor.

Other system components consist of: a hot wire air flow mass meter, a standard three-wire variable output throttle potentiometer mounted directly on the throttle shaft, a standard NTC-type coolant sensor in the water jacket just below the distributor at the rear of the head and a Lambda sensor fitted right at the top of the exhaust downpipe, at the front of the engine.

Immediately below the Lambda sensor is the catalytic converter which is positioned very close to the engine. Known accordingly as a 'close-coupled cat.', the big benefits of this approach are that it warms quickly and, in addition, enjoys greater protection – conventional, under-floor locations are subjected to excess wind rush, water spray and the possibility of impact damage. The disadvantage is that under extreme conditions it can become overheated and suffer thermal breakdown.

It is also worth noting that the Lambda sensor is heated – unusual for a sensor combined with a close-coupled cat. Frank assumes that the designers realised that the Micra would be predominantly a town car and so made doubly sure that the cat. would be as efficient as possible.

There is a dual idle control system consisting of an auxiliary air valve which operates during cold starting, and a fast idle control. The latter is a stepper motor used to enhance idle speed when the system is loaded by power steering operation or electrical systems etc. Both of these are combined within the same unit found on the air intake venturi.

The fuel pump is integral within the tank and its relay is found behind a kick panel in the driver's footwell (on the right). The main ECU relay is mounted in a box close to the battery under the bonnet.

Other notable features include a carbon canister which is used to soak up excessive fuel vapour from the tank, and then feed it back into the induction manifold under conditions of acceleration when it is most needed. Also there is an electronic road speed sensor which sends a digital signal to the ECU to influence overrun fuel control and engine idle performance. It also regulates the carbon canister, preventing needless operation when the vehicle is stationary but throttle is blipped.

The good news, from a DIY point of view, is that the ECCS system is code-readable without the need for any specialist equipment, via a light on the dash or a red LED on the ECU itself – mounted just behind the centre console.

A 14-pin diagnostic socket, tucked away behind a panel on the right lower dash, is used to initiate the code check procedure. With the ignition on, but without the engine running, two terminals of this socket – denoted 'ign' and 'chk' – must be bridged. They are the two at the left-hand end of the bottom row, when viewed from the front, on this Micra application. Beware this positioning varies on other Nissan models.

According to Frank the terminals can be bridged with a bent paper clip, which should be held in place for at least two seconds then disconnected. At this point self-diagnosis mode will have been selected. After this simply count the flashes (ECU LED or dash light) and relate to the fault code reference. All codes are simple two-digit – eg. 12 is represented by, flash, pause, then two flashes in quick succession.

There are about 24 codes in the system and while this does not provide comprehensive cover, Frank says that in common with most Japanese applications, they are reliable. Switching the ignition off reverts the system back to standard mode – no other adjustments are required.

---

to the efficient recirculation of the crankcase gases and residual pressure.

Consequently, it is rare to find any carbon contamination within the venturi/throttle body located under the main air filter housing. In the event that you do find some then be careful when trying to remove it. The 'hot wires' within the venturi which relate air mass information are very sensitive. They are protected by a metal gauze across the top and you should not be tempted to remove this and use a brush to tackle the deposits because you will do damage. A carburettor cleaning spray should be sufficient says Frank.

In addition, it is important that the protective gauze is present and intact. Frank says that damage to it will alter the air flow characteristics and detrimentally vary the output from the air mass meter.

Vacuum hoses normally abound on Japanese engines and all should be checked for any obvious problems. But as Frank points out, generally the qual-ity of these rubber bits is excellent and few problems should be encountered with perished or degraded pipework.

Because the system relies on an air mass meter the main air induction sys-tem is not really an influencing factor on mixture so air leaks here are not a desperate problem.

The distributor is an important area and must be treated with care. Within

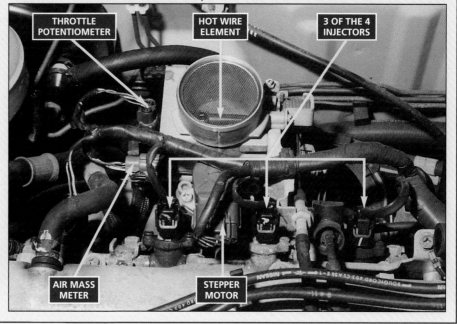

THROTTLE POTENTIOMETER — HOT WIRE ELEMENT — 3 OF THE 4 INJECTORS — AIR MASS METER — STEPPER MOTOR

ELECTRONIC DIAGNOSTICS!

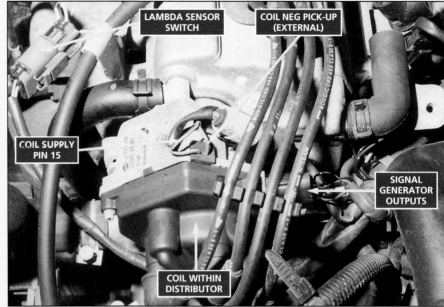

the cap there are the signal generators already mentioned plus a rotor arm containing laser-cut slots and mounted on a rotating spindle. A static LED and photo-cell assembly react to the spinning disc.

The sensitivity of the disc and sensors means that its performance is determined by its cleanliness. Just a little dust can cause genuine engine trouble – just a smattering can be sufficient to generate misfires. If you find this then gently blow out the assembly with an air line. If this does not cure the problem then apply a carburettor cleaning spray and blow dry – never use a brush.

The only way that the output of the signal generator (speed/position) can be checked is by using an oscilloscope. A multimeter will not be good enough because it will tend to average out the switching and will not provide a definitive check. It is vital to establish the quality of the switching action – not only must it have the correct ground reference and supply but it must also switch perfectly 'cleanly'. This must be observed on a scope screen so that the square, digital switch can be meaningfully assessed.

The cap itself should be simply washed, blown dry and checked for cracks and any obvious signs of corrosion on the terminals. Treat the rotor arm similarly. Problems in the cap are not common because usually a vacuum hose runs from it to the inlet manifold which effectively prevents the build up of potentially damaging gases.

Plug leads are effectively routed so few problems should occur with these. However, it's always worth checking for damage to the boots caused by careless handling with pliers etc.

Remove and inspect the plugs. Because this system is multipoint, all the plug tips should appear identical. Ideally the electrodes should be very clean and almost white in colour, while the surrounding body of the plug will be dark. Be aware also that incorrect plugs can cause signal interference problems, especially if non-resistive ones have been fitted instead of resistive, for example.

If you find uneven plug appearance then suspect initially air leaks. Use a vacuum gauge to establish manifold vacuum. This should be well above 20in/Hg and often nearer 22in/Hg with the engine at idle – always good on Japanese engines. If this is not the problems then turn to the injectors. Remove them and send them to be tested on a flow bench for delivery rate and spray pattern.

Another good indicator on this engine, as with all cat-equipped motors, is provided by the switching action of the Lambda sensor. This always provides an excellent 'window' into the way the engine is performing. Incorrect switching will lead to poor fuel economy and generally flat performance. In this case the sensor is a standard three-wire zirconium component which switches from 200mV to 800mV, and should do this at a frequency of well above one hertz. The one we sampled here was switching at two hertz so was very efficient.

In addition, the signal from the Lambda sensor should be spending equal time in the 'go rich' and 'go lean' zones. If the switching rate is out then suspect air leaks or injector performance. Be sure about both before

TECHNICAL SPECIFICATIONS

Throttle potentiometer	Supply – 5V Earth – 0.25V Output – 0.7-4.5V
Air mass meter	Supply – 12+V (green wire) Earth – 0.25V (black wire) Output static 0.3V Idle 1.18V Cruise 2.0V Open throttle 4.0V
Crank angle sensor	Supply – 12V (green/black wire) Speed/position output – 5V digital (white) Earth – 0.25V (black wire x 2) Timing pulse – 3.5V digital (red/orange)
Stepper motor	Supply – 12V (pink wire) Earth – 0.25V (black wire) Output cold idle 30 to-30V, @ 160Hz (red) cold idle 30-0V @ 16-Hz (bwn/yell) cold idle 30-0V @ 160Hz (black/yell)
Coolant sensor	Output cold 3.5V hot 1.0V
Lambda sensor	Supply – 12V (white wire) Earth – 0.25V (white wire) Output – 0.2-0.8V @ 2+Hz (black wire)
Injector duration (sequential saturated drive pulse)	2.5-3ms hot idle 3-4ms cold idle 15ms snap load 8-10ms during cranking 0.5ms on static overrun
Fuel pressure	2.5 bar with vacuum 3.0 bar without vacuum
Fule flow rate	60+ litres/hour
Ignition timing	15° @ 600rpm (manual car) 15° @ 700rpm (automatic car)

Photo labels: LAMBDA SENSOR SWITCH; COIL NEG PICK-UP (EXTERNAL); COIL SUPPLY PIN 15; SIGNAL GENERATOR OUTPUTS; COIL WITHIN DISTRIBUTOR

Here Frank is pointing at the ECCS ECU. Just above his left ear is the compartment containing the 14-pin diagnostic socked used for initiating the fault code check procedure.

will happen again.

The idle control valve exhibits a fairly unusual waveform output. It is digital but has a positive and negative slope. The polarity of the component is being repeatedly reversed. There is a vertical rise of +30V, followed by a gradual tale off down to about 10V. It then switched to negative polarity and drops straight to -30V, followed by a gradual rise to about -10V. This switching action is fast, running at 160hz with the engine at idle.

Another possibility for future trouble with this system relates to its relative complexity. The fact that multiple inputs are required magnifies the potential likelihood for trouble. Even a component as simple as a throttle potentiometer can cause what appear to be reasonably complex problems.

The information from the pot. influences primary factors such as correct idle speed on overrun, acceleration enrichment and closed loop emission control. Poor output can lead to hesitation, unsatisfactory low-speed drivability and other fuel-related defects. These sorts of problem can point convincingly towards a fault with the ECU when in reality they are being caused by nothing more than dirt contamination in the pot.

Check it carefully by hand, using an oscilloscope for the best results. Range it across its track and watch for glitches

blaming the sensor itself.

If downstream measurements throw up problems with emissions, and the Lambda sensor is switching as it should, then the cat. is at fault. Remember, however, not to simply replace it without establishing the cause of its failure, otherwise the same thing

in output. Remember, also, that pots. can be adversely affected by heat and vibration so may not show a fault in the calm workshop environment.

THE SERIES SO FAR

No.1	Basic systems – **July 1994**
No.2	Diagnostic equipment – **August 1994**
No.3	Test preparation – **September 1994**
No.4	Ford 2.0i – **October 1994**
No.5	Rover 200/400 – **November 1994**
No.6	Vauxhall 2.0i – **December 1994**
No.7	Peugeot 205/309 GTi – **January 1995**
No.8	Ford 2.9i V6 – **February 1995**
No.9	BMW 1.8i – **March 1995**
No.10	Vauxhall 2.0i 16v – **April 1995**
No.11	Rover 2.0i 16v – **May 1995**
No.12	Rover 1.6/2.0 EFi – **June 1995**
No.13	Rover 1.6/2.0 ignition – **July 1995**
No.14	Ford Zeta 16v – **August 1995**
No.15	VW 1.8 Digifant – **September 1995**
No.16	Honda Legend/Rover 800 – **October 1995**
No.17	Ford XR2i/RS Turbo – **November 1995**
No.18	Peugeot 405 Mi16 – **December 1995**
No.19	Renault Clio 1.2i – **January 1996**
No.20	Vauxhall 24v – **February 1996**
No.21	Range Rover V8 – **March 1996**
No.22	Honda Civic 1.6 – **April 1996**
No.23	Rover 820 single point – **May 1996**
No.24	Jaguar 3.6 straight six – **June 1996**
No.25	Audi 80 – **July 1996**
No.26	Ford Escort/Fiesta – **August 1996**
No.27	Vauxhall 1.8i – **September 1996**
No.28	Saab 900/9000 – **November 1996**
No.29	VW Digifant update – **December 1996**
No.30	Vauxhall Ecotec – **January 1997**

NEXT MONTH
Peugeot 405 2-litre.

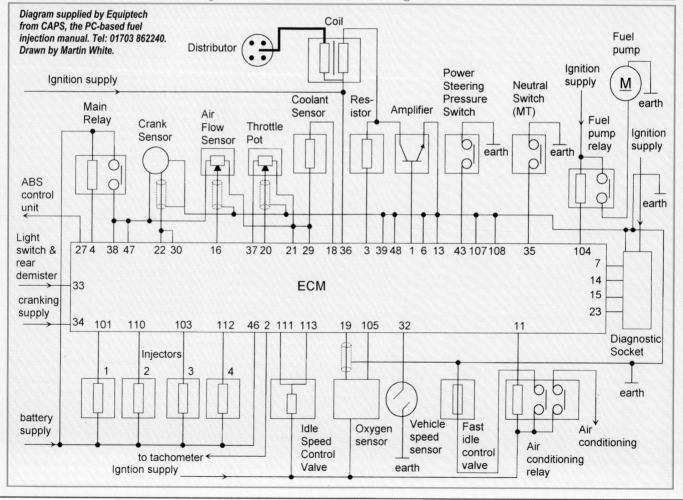

Diagram supplied by Equiptech from CAPS, the PC-based fuel injection manual. Tel: 01703 862240. Drawn by Martin White.

ELECTRONIC DIAGNOSTICS!

How to trace faults in electronic engine management systems

Number 32: The popular Peugeot 405 1.8i uses Bosch Motronic MP5.1 engine management. Chris Graham focuses on its foibles

In common with Renault and Citroën, Peugeot tend to chop and change engine management more than most manufacturers. Across all three ranges you will find an assortment of systems from Bosch, Magneti-Marelli and Bendix Fenix.

Since 1988 Peugeot have used eight different systems so, as Fuel Injection Services' Frank Massey (Tel: 01772 201597) pointed out, the first task is to establish precisely which system you

---

POTENTIAL PROBLEMS
1. **Unstable idle**
2. **Hesitation**
3. **MAP sensor**

---

are dealing with.

The late 405 1.8i featured here makes use of Bosch Motronic MP5.1 and, being a Bosch system, this one can be double-checked using a hand-held fault tester such as the Sykes-Pickavant

Advanced Code Reader. With the correct software pod this tool will identify the system before doing anything else.

Unfortunately, this is not possible with the non-Bosch systems so you will have to rely on other sources of data for accurate identification.

The good news is that so far MP5.1, on this application, is proving very reliable. Frank has yet to see any significant faults relating to serious system breakdown.

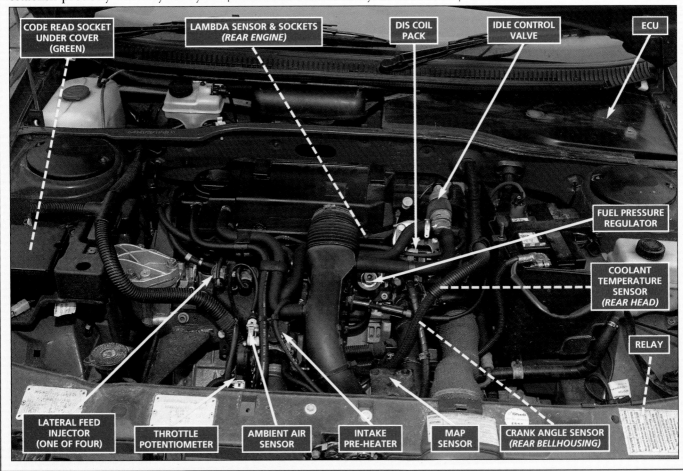

CODE READ SOCKET UNDER COVER (GREEN) — LAMBDA SENSOR & SOCKETS (REAR ENGINE) — DIS COIL PACK — IDLE CONTROL VALVE — ECU — FUEL PRESSURE REGULATOR — COOLANT TEMPERATURE SENSOR (REAR HEAD) — RELAY — LATERAL FEED INJECTOR (ONE OF FOUR) — THROTTLE POTENTIOMETER — AMBIENT AIR SENSOR — INTAKE PRE-HEATER — MAP SENSOR — CRANK ANGLE SENSOR (REAR BELLHOUSING)

ENGINE MANAGEMENT

Bosch Motronic MP5.1 provides total engine management on this 1.8-litre 405 application. It arrived in 1992 and is also found on 306 models with 1.6 and 1.8-litre engines – as well as corresponding Citroën models.

A single 37-pin ECU manages ignition and fuelling and, in keeping with most modern system configurations, it runs with a so called 'wasted spark' DIS ignition. This is essentially a solid state system consisting of a simple twin-coil pack and no distributor as such – no rotor arm or other moving parts to worry about. The pack is triggered directly from the ECU.

The fuel injection is multipoint with four laterally-fed injectors, which means that there is no requirement for a conventional fuel rail. The big benefit of this is that the incoming fuel surrounds the injectors and keeps them cool, assisting hot starting performance.

One interesting general point is that the induction manifold is made from plastic. This is unusual and Frank believes that,

apart from being a cheaper component to manufacture, it boasts superior heat dissipation properties compared to the conventional metal component.

Primary system components consist of: a standard two-wire coolant temperature sensor at the back of the cylinder head; an ambient air temperature sensor positioned in the air induction system; an external three-wire MAP sensor located at the front on a bracket attached to the front panel; a catalytic converter and a standard four-wire, zirconium-type Lambda sensor fitted in the downpipe.

Also there is: a crank angle sensor, located at the back of the bell housing, which provides the basic input to the ECU for the whole system – triggered by a conventional phonic wheel; a rotary idle control valve under direct ECU command; four laterally-fed fuel injectors running intermittently – all switched by a common output from the ECU in response to the basic engine speed, load and temperature

inputs; a tachiomatic relay for the fuel pump; an air intake pre-heater (often called a 'hedgehog') to warm inducted air and a standard three-wire throttle potentiometer.

The system has diagnostic capability via a socket under the bonnet. There are approximately 40 actual fault codes programmed within the system and any which may be logged can be accessed using a code reader. In addition, a simpler LED tester can be used as a cheaper alternative and this will generate countable blink codes.

Via serial communications it is also possible to drive certain important components including the fuel pump, ignition coil, carbon canister solenoid and fuel injectors. There is also the capability to monitor component performance directly – factors such as voltage, temperature or switch time etc.

However, because the system is fully closed-loop there is no ignition timing or fuel mixture adjustment facility at all. Idle speed, too, is set automatically.

Preparation

Because of the relatively simple nature of the DIS ignition system, apart from inspecting the leads there is very little to be done in terms of general preparation work. Content yourself with checking the plug leads for chafing or cut damage but be aware that this is pretty unlikely because all are well routed and protected by a conduit.

However, Frank warns that the DIS system does pack a serious electrical punch. The unwary should note that you can expect 60,000+V to be buzzing around so it's vitally important that leads, boots and joints are in good order to contain any problems. Electrical spikes of this magnitude will seriously damage other electrical components (as well as carelessly probing humans) so be warned!

Always inspect the plugs for correct gapping and type – refer to owners manual if in any doubt. Don't fall into the trap of simply replacing like with like without checking first.

On the air intake side Frank recommends removing the idle control valve and washing it out with carburettor cleaner, followed by light lubrication. Check also the throttle induction system and make sure that the disc is clean. Cast an eye over the throttle stop too – somebody may have tweaked it which will throw the throttle potentiometer voltage out of range.

Make sure also that the throttle cable is adjusted correctly, showing the recommended amount of play. While you're at it, check that the linkage operates freely too.

Watch out for air leaks in the important vacuum hose which runs be-

tween the inlet manifold and the MAP sensor at the front of the engine bay in the centre – the condition of this is crucial. Be on your guard for kinks in the pipe, cuts and other surface damage and check that it is a snug fit at each end. If not then Frank says that there is usually enough slack to allow the weakened end to be cut off so that a fresh section can be pushed home tightly. Peek inside the pipe too. Trapped oil or petrol in there can provide enough of a restriction to inhibit the response of the MAP sensor, varying its voltage output.

Finally, Frank advises that if you intend carrying out specific tests – cranking balance etc. – on the DIS ignition system, and producing a full diagnostic report, then special equipment kits (software and hardware) will make the job a lot easier. These are commercially available through the specialists suppliers.

Problem solving

We've already established that Motronic MP5.1 is a reasonably reliable application. Serious faults are very rare but Frank has come across a number of possible areas of concern.

The first relates to poor engine idle and is highlighted by the triggering of the engine management light plus the logging of fault code number 21. This relates to a problem with the throttle potentiometer and Frank says that the official advice is to change it without question. His approach, however, is less cavalier – he always likes to make sure of the cause before swapping expensive components.

This pot. is a simple component providing a straightforward analogue voltage output. It ranges from 0.5 to 4.5V and this should be achieved in a smooth, progressive transition. It is

Bosch Motronic MP5.1 has serial communication capability when linked to test equipment such as Sykes-Pickavant's excellent Advanced Code Reader. Diagnostic socket is under black cover on offside inner wing.

easy to test. The essential factor is to make sure that the output is 'clean' and that it ranges correctly.

Always check throttle pots. by hand with the ignition switched on. You can work with a meter for this test if it is a good one and has a 'glitch catching' capability. Variations in the output need only be small to create a problem and, usually, basic meters are not capable of spotting them. The ultimate, of course, is to use an oscilloscope because this will catch any electrical glitches for sure, but will also highlight any 'noise' on the signal.

Electrical noise can cause problems even if the actual voltage output is as it should be. It will be interpreted by the ECU as an erratic output which can lead directly to poor idle valve control. An additional side effect could well be that excessive fuel will be brought in.

Most modern systems now rely on throttle pot. voltage outputs as an early warning indicator of impending acceleration. So another symptom of the problem can be over-fuelling.

One slight complication is the fact that there are now two pots. available for this application, one is a later version with the part number PR1920-0F. Frank assumes from this introduction that the original component must have

ECU and main relays located under black cover on nearside engine bulkhead.

suffered from some inherent fault, either electrical or mechanical, which led to derivability problems on the car.

Unfortunately, there is no prospect for cleaning or repairing the throttle potentiometer. It is a sealed unit and so replacement really is the only option if a genuine problem is found – Frank believes that new ones cost about £40-50.

Hesitation with a cold engine and perhaps even backfires through the inlet manifold, can be another problem with this system. Frank's interpretation of this is a simple lack of fuel. He says that modified ECUs with upgraded software variants are available from specialist suppliers (such as ATP, tel: 01543 467466) but before going to these lengths his advice is always to check the injectors.

They should be removed, tested and cleaned to check for correct performance. Because they are of the laterally-fed variety some specialists may not have the Asnu testing equipment needed but all good ones should.

If the injectors pass the test but the problem remains then you will have to investigate the software route. Frank says that ATP will modify an existing ECU for less than the £200-300 needed to buy a complete outright unit. Other obvious checks should include making sure that there are no air leaks in the system which could be causing the lean mixture.

Often these sorts of problem will only become apparent once the engine starts to age and has covered a high mileage. The build-up of carbon on the backs of the valves plus increasing levels of general engine wear are both factors which play a part.

Problems with the MAP sensor are another distinct possibility, in particular its output accuracy. Obviously because these vehicles are all fitted with catalytic converters and run total closed-loop emission control systems, they are subject to the tighter emission test regulations at the MoT test.

If you find a car which has failed this test on emissions and appears to be fuelling badly – either lean or rich – before you dive in and blame the Lambda sensor for poor response performance, it is well worth checking the MAP sensor output.

This can be done statically using a vacuum pump but it is essential that the pump is correctly calibrated – the readings it produces must be accurate. You should work carefully through the range in which the sensor operates checking the voltage all the while. In

TECHNICAL SPECIFICATIONS

Crank angle sensor	Sine wave self-inductive Cranking – 5-10V peak to peak Idle – 20V peak to peak
Coolant temperature sensor	NTC-type Output – 3-3.5V cold, 0.5-0.8V hot
Ambient air temp. sensor	Output 3-3.5V
MAP sensor	Atmospheric pressure – 4.5V Idle – 1.1-1.3V, 18-20in/Hg Overrun – 0.6V, 23-25in/Hg
Lambda sensor	12V heater supply Switching 200-800mV @ 1Hz+
Throttle potentiometer	Closed – 0.5V With throttle open – 4.5V
Idle control valve	12V digital output 100Hz duty cycle variation
Injector duration	Hot – 2.5ms Cold – 4ms Snap load – 8-16+ms Cold cranking – 8ms
Fuel pressure	Vacuum off – 3 bar Vacuum on – 2.5 bar
Fuel flow rate	60lt/hr or better

ECU update
Original ECU Nos. – 0216 200 664/665/666/67
ATP replacement No. – XEBM 0666

THE SERIES SO FAR

No.1	Basic systems – **July 1994**
No.2	Diagnostic equipment – **August 1994**
No.3	Test preparation – **September 1994**
No.4	Ford 2.0i – **October 1994**
No.5	Rover 200/400 – **November 1994**
No.6	Vauxhall 2.0i – **December 1994**
No.7	Peugeot 205/309 GTi – **January 1995**
No.8	Ford 2.9i V6 – **February 1995**
No.9	BMW 1.8i – **March 1995**
No.10	Vauxhall 2.0i 16v – **April 1995**
No.11	Rover 2.0i 16v – **May 1995**
No.12	Rover 1.6/2.0 EFi – **June 1995**
No.13	Rover 1.6/2.0 ignition – **July 1995**
No.14	Ford Zeta 16v – **August 1995**
No.15	VW 1.8 Digifant – **September 1995**
No.16	Honda Legend/Rover 800 – **October 1995**
No.17	Ford XR2i/RS Turbo – **November 1995**
No.18	Peugeot 405 Mi16 – **December 1995**
No.19	Renault Clio 1.2i – **January 1996**
No.20	Vauxhall 24v – **February 1996**
No.21	Range Rover V8 – **March 1996**
No.22	Honda Civic 1.6 – **April 1996**
No.23	Rover 820 single point – **May 1996**
No.24	Jaguar 3.6 straight six – **June 1996**
No.25	Audi 80 – **July 1996**
No.26	Ford Escort/Fiesta – **August 1996**
No.27	Vauxhall 1.8i – **September 1996**
No.28	Saab 900/9000 – **November 1996**
No.29	VW Digifant update – **December 1996**
No.30	Vauxhall Ecotec – **January 1997**
No.31	Nissan Micra 16V – **February 1997**

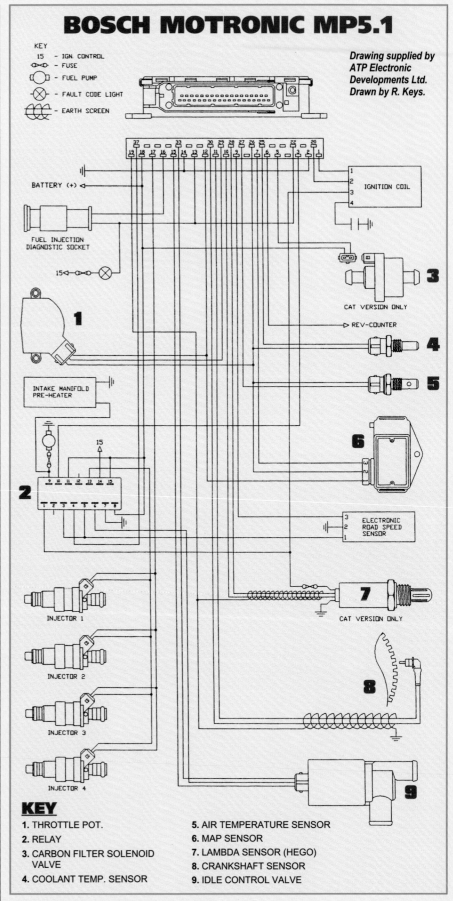

BOSCH MOTRONIC MP5.1

KEY
15 – IGN. CONTROL
– FUSE
– FUEL PUMP
– FAULT CODE LIGHT
– EARTH SCREEN

Drawing supplied by
ATP Electronic
Developments Ltd.
Drawn by R. Keys.

BATTERY (+)

FUEL INJECTION
DIAGNOSTIC SOCKET

15

INTAKE MANIFOLD
PRE-HEATER

15

IGNITION COIL

CAT VERSION ONLY

REV-COUNTER

ELECTRONIC
ROAD SPEED
SENSOR

INJECTOR 1

INJECTOR 2

INJECTOR 3

INJECTOR 4

CAT VERSION ONLY

KEY
1. THROTTLE POT.
2. RELAY
3. CARBON FILTER SOLENOID VALVE
4. COOLANT TEMP. SENSOR
5. AIR TEMPERATURE SENSOR
6. MAP SENSOR
7. LAMBDA SENSOR (HEGO)
8. CRANKSHAFT SENSOR
9. IDLE CONTROL VALVE

addition, as well as checking that the voltage tolerance is correct, you must make sure that the values are stable.

The output from the MAP sensor is critical and so even slight deviations from specification will make a significant difference. Values as small as 0.25V too high or too low will have a noticeable effect on the fuelling of the engine – it really is that tight. Fundamental problems with MAP sensor output will only be cured by replacing the component. New ones cost about £100.

If output is found to be OK but the fuelling continues to be wrong then obviously the problem must be elsewhere. At this point switch your attention to the Lambda (oxygen) sensor and check fuel pressure too.

The sensor is of the zirconium variety and switches between 0.2 and 0.8V at a frequency of one hertz or faster – preferably two hertz – ideally with a smooth transition between the rich and lean sectors of the signal. In addition, the balance of the switching action is important. Frank says the sensor's output should spend equal time on 'go rich' and 'go lean' commands.

Of course, a scope is essential for carrying out this level of sensor performance assessment. Lambda sensors, as they age, tend to become lazy and reduce in switching frequency. This has a detrimental effect on drivability when the engine is hot and shows up as gentle surging when cruising on a light throttle setting.

Finally, as we have stressed before, always be wary if advised simply to change the ECU. This can be an 'official' recommendation but Frank warns that it should never be agreed to if alternative methods of correction have not been explored.

For example, if the problem is poor fuelling then it makes far more sense to check the injectors, and even consider a decoke, before opting to swap the control unit. Remember that ECUs are inherently reliable components and so genuine problems are rare.

NEXT MONTH
Volvo 940 2-litre.

ELECTRONIC DIAGNOSTICS!

How to trace faults in electronic engine management systems

Number 33: At long last we investigate our first Volvo in this series. Chris Graham reports on the 940 2.0-litre.

Considering its age, the management set-up on this Volvo 940 application is unusual because it features separate fuel injection and ignition control systems – most vehicles are on total engine management now. It is one of the last of a dying breed – an old fashioned new car!

The first problem, therefore, is to establish in which system the fault is. Frank Massey, proprietor at Preston-based Fuel Injection Services (Tel: 01772 201597) says that trouble can

TYPICAL FAULTS
1. **Over fuelling**
2. **Loss of spark**
3. **Lean mixture**

strike in either the fuel or the ignition systems, or a combination of the two. Some components, the coolant sensor for example, are shared.

Both systems are made by Bosch and first appeared on 940 and 960 2- and 2.3-litre models in 1990. The ignition is Bosch EZ 116K, which Frank con-

siders to be a competent stand-alone system with all the features of a modern engine management package. Control is based on engine speed, load and temperature inputs, plus crankshaft position. The system is also code readable and has knock control.

The fuelling is Bosch LH Jetronic 2.4 which is also code readable and generally performs well. The system as a whole is essentially reliable but, Frank warns that because it makes use of the older style components, age-related defects are always a risk.

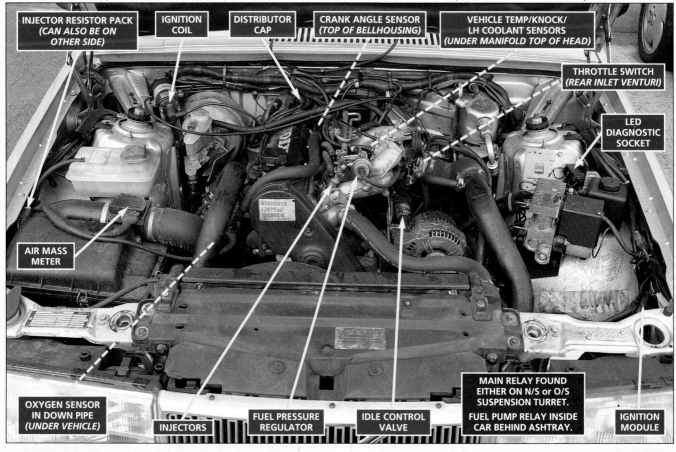

INJECTOR RESISTOR PACK (CAN ALSO BE ON OTHER SIDE)

IGNITION COIL

DISTRIBUTOR CAP

CRANK ANGLE SENSOR (TOP OF BELLHOUSING)

VEHICLE TEMP/KNOCK/ LH COOLANT SENSORS (UNDER MANIFOLD TOP OF HEAD)

THROTTLE SWITCH (REAR INLET VENTURI)

LED DIAGNOSTIC SOCKET

AIR MASS METER

OXYGEN SENSOR IN DOWN PIPE (UNDER VEHICLE)

INJECTORS

FUEL PRESSURE REGULATOR

IDLE CONTROL VALVE

MAIN RELAY FOUND EITHER ON N/S or O/S SUSPENSION TURRET. FUEL PUMP RELAY INSIDE CAR BEHIND ASHTRAY.

IGNITION MODULE

ENGINE MANAGEMENT

The fuelling side of the system relies on multipoint injection, with one injector per cylinder, working intermittently. Each is controlled by a common output from the main LH ECU, found inside the car behind a kick panel in the driver's footwell.

Idle control is provided by a rotary idle control valve and another blast from the past is the cold start valve – found at the back of the inlet manifold. This is designed to operate at temperatures below -20°C and so rarely works in the UK climate.

The main components on the fuelling side of the system include: a throttle switch, rather than a potentiometer, mounted on the throttle spindle next to the induction venturi; a dual relay powering up the ECU and fuel pump; an air mass meter (with no adjustment potential on cat-equipped cars) in the main air induction system between the air filter and inlet manifold; the aforementioned two-wire rotary idle control valve which bypasses the throttle disc; a coolant sensor found at the front, top of the cylinder head on the n/s under the inlet manifold.

Basic input to trigger the injectors comes from the EZ ignition unit and must be a stable signal. A phonic wheel on the flywheel induces the crank angle sensor which, in turn, transmits the results to the EZ ignition's own ECU – found inside, under the offside dash tray. A separate digital trigger emerges from the EZ control unit and is sent directly to pin 1 on the Bosch LH ECU where it is used as a basis for injector timing.

Because two seperate digital triggers are sent from EZ pin 16 amp trigger and pin 17 LH trigger, some confusion may arise if one or both systems go down, so take care. Frank says there will be cases where you will observe good ignition performance but loss of the trigger output to the LH ECU. This can still be an ignition fault within the EZ box. So never assume that just because the coil is working correctly that all is well with the EZ unit. The trigger it sends to the LH system is fundamental. It must be present and correct.

A further complication is that there are two different ignition modules used for this EZ system, and they are not interchangeable. Fit the wrong one and the vehicle will not run. Frank believes that the difference relates to pin configuration.

Fundamentally the ignition system is conventional with a distributor cap mounted at the back of the engine and a standard coil. However, the cap suffers badly with contamination and is fitted with a plastic cover which traps dirt and moisture. Problems here can cause electrical spikes to jump back to the control units which causes trouble.

As far as fault diagnostics is concerned there is a code indicator under the bonnet for extracting fault codes via a flashing LED. Sykes-Pickavant produce a Volvo software pod for their Advanced Code Reader which provides full access to the system. A further alternative is provided by Autodiagnos (Tel: 01772 887774) whose equipment and software originates from Sweden, where it was developed specifically for Volvo applications.

Frank says that this really is the best available for this and similarly-specified applications. It allows for the monitoring of live data, including injector duration, air mass meter output, Lambda switching etc. The cost is about £3,000.

Preparation

The good news is that this engine is not generally a very dirty unit and most tend to run pretty oil free. However, this is not to say that it is without its share of dirt-related problems. Primary among these is distributor cap contamination.

This is an extremely common problem on this application – the car is second only to the Vauxhall Carlton in this respect! So, without a doubt, your first prep job should be to take off and discard the ineffective plastic cover (if it's still there) then remove and inspect the distributor cap.

Rotor arms tend to lead a hard life so check carefully for body cracking and erosion on the tip. You may find some which are 'locked' into position and cannot be removed without force. In these cases Frank has no hesitation about cracking them off – he always fits a new one as a matter of course anyway.

Inspect the HT leads for the usual problems – chafing, heat damage etc. They are routed across the exhaust manifold and so are forced to operate in a harsh environment.

The coil also tends to suffer with dirt and other contamination. Wash and dry it carefully. Another component to suffer is the ignition module. This is an external amplifier unit (in addition to the EZ control unit) which boosts the EZ's output to the ignition coil.

Unfortunately, this vital component is positioned at the front of the car, just behind the n/s headlamp, with its socket facing skywards. It nestles per-fectly below the gap between the bonnet edge and wing and gets regularly watered. Consequently, water gets into the socket causing corrosion of the terminals, leading to electrical shorts and/or high resistances. Always remove and inspect this socket.

Although it is fitted with a rubber boot plus an internal rubber gasket, water still works its way inside. Once you have cleaned it out thoroughly, Frank's advice is to pack it with a quality water repellent product such as Vaseline.

Don't forget the rotary idle control valve either. This too should be removed, washed or soaked as necessary, lightly lubricated and replaced. The throttle switch is adjustable and must be checked. With the ICV removed, make sure that the throttle stop has not been incorrectly adjusted. Back it off until the throttle jams, 'crack' it off the seat, lock it and then set the switch. This operates with an audible click and should be set so that it clicks the moment the throttle starts to open. However, make sure the voltage is switching too – faulty ones can click without switching electrically.

Remove and inspect the spark plugs as these will give a very good indication of how well the engine is running. Make sure that the correct ones are fitted, that the gaps are right and that you replace them as necessary.

Finally, keep an eye on the condition of the exhaust manifold. Its integrity is important as we'll see later – air leaks can lead to fuelling problems.

Fault finding

One of the most common faults with this system is engine over-fuelling. Unfortunately, Frank says that there are

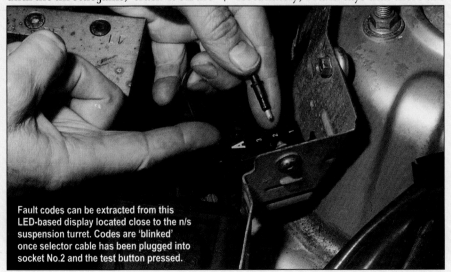

Fault codes can be extracted from this LED-based display located close to the n/s suspension turret. Codes are 'blinked' once selector cable has been plugged into socket No.2 and the test button pressed.

ELECTRONIC DIAGNOSTICS!

many possible causes. Often the problem will present itself at the MoT test when exhaust emissions fail to meet the required standard. The owner may also complain of unusually high fuel consumption – both are typical indicators.

If you discover that the vehicle has been previously fiddled with, and that a new coolant sensor has been fitted, then make this sensor your first check. It is a very important component because it's shared by both ignition and fuelling systems – temperature input is essential for both ECUs.

Frank explains that it is a dual sensor containing two resistive elements. It finds earth through the engine's cylinder head, via its own body. If it is mistakenly replaced with a single-element sensor (the standard type used nowadays for most other applications) the wrong resistive values will be sent to both ignition and fuelling ECUs. While the effects on ignition will not be too serious, on the fuelling side such a mistake will generate incorrect injector values so durations will be wrong.

As far a checking the sensor type is concerned Frank, for once, advises referring to resistances. Remove the sensor and test the resistance between the engine block and each of its pins. This should be about 3,500 ohms when cold and 300 ohms when hot. If not then suspect that the wrong sensor has been fitted and replace it.

Another very common cause of over-fuelling is a drift in the output value of the air mass meter. Deviations of as little as 0.25V from the norm can be sufficient to upset fuelling. However, in addition to the actual signal

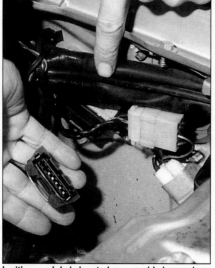

Ignition module is located on nearside inner wing, immediately below bonnet edge gap. Water ingress into socket is a real problem.

value its quality is vital too. It must be 'clean' (no electrical noise) and to check this you will need an oscilloscope.

Tolerances are pretty fine and distortions as relatively small as 200-300MV can be sufficient to disturb the ECU and, in turn, lead to fuelling problems. If you find the signal is being disturbed, and you have checked all relevant earths, and for interference from the ignition circuits and alternator, then the only solution is to replace the air mass meter.

It relies on a heated wire for its operation and the condition of this wire is obviously essential to overall performance. It can become contaminated and so de-sensitised to the vital cooling effect of the air being drawn over it. To guard against this the system operates a regular 'burn off' function. A current of five volts is fired down the wire – on engine shut down – to rapidly heat it and displace any dirt which may have lodged there.

Failure of this mechanism will cause

problems but it is sensed, so a fault code will be generated warning of such a problem. Never attempt to clean an air mass meter hot wire with a brush, it is far too fragile for this. The only realistic alternative is to seek out a professional with ultrasonic cleaning equipment. Replacement meters cost about £250.

Loss of spark can be another relatively common problem, often linked to the failure of the ignition module. Possible causes can be voltage induction from the HT circuit – tracking back from the distributor cap or coil, both of which get seriously dirty. Water ingress is the other primary cause. Unfortunately, there is not enough spare wire to turn the component over and protect the normally exposed socket from the deluge. Re-locating it is a possibility although Frank has not tried this. Failure normally means replacement – new modules cost about £130 (Bosch).

The third common problem relates to lean mixture and is often accompanied by the triggering of the dash-mounted warning light. This lamp relates specifically to the Lambda sensor which, in itself, is unusual. However, Frank says that in many cases simply changing the sensor does no good at all. Assuming that all the wiring is good, then the root of the complaint is an exhaust manifold air leak. Because this system runs with closed loop control, and is fitted with a catalytic converter, the integrity of the exhaust manifold is vital.

Remember that, in practice, it takes very little extra air to cause a problem within the system. Even slight leaks around the flange can be sufficient to upset the balance and cracks in the manifold or downpipe itself will certainly lead to trouble.

The oxygen sensor reacts to the extra air, defines it as a lean mixture and sends a 'go rich' signal to the ECU. The result is an over-fuelling situation, not because of a fault with the engine, or any of the sensors, but simply because of an air leak.

With such a problem it can be possible that the emissions at the tailpipe will still be OK because, although working hard, the cat will be effectively compensating for the imbalance. Despite this, fuel consumption will suffer and the spark plugs will appear black and sootier than normal. All problems

TECHNICAL SPECIFICATIONS

Coolant sensor	3.5V cold, 0.5-1V hot. *(Note: This is a dual sensor with chassis earth)*
Idle control valve	Digital switching, 12V to ground, at 100Hz.
Cold start valve	Not used in UK (climate too warm!)
Air mass meter	Variable output according to load. 1.7V static (ignition on) 2.7V at idle 3.2V at 3,000rpm
Burn off (AMM hot wire)	Hot engine/2,500+rpm, switch off then 5V for one second.
Lambda sensor	Zirconium oxide type 200-800MV at 1Hz+.
Idle contact	Switching Pin 2, 12V to ground. Full load (if used) Pin 3, ground to 12V.
Injector resistor pack	Battery voltage input from main relay. Approx. 9V output, only when injector on.
Injector duration	3-4ms cold, 2.2-2.5ms hot, 10-12ms during cold cranking.

THE SERIES SO FAR

No.1   Basic systems – **July 1994**
No.2   Diagnostic equipment – **August 1994**
No.3   Test preparation – **September 1994**
No.4   Ford 2.0i – **October 1994**
No.5   Rover 200/400 – **November 1994**
No.6   Vauxhall 2.0i – **December 1994**
No.7   Peugeot 205/309 GTi – **January 1995**
No.8   Ford 2.9i V6 – **February 1995**
No.9   BMW 1.8i – **March 1995**
No.10 Vauxhall 2.0i 16v – **April 1995**
No.11 Rover 2.0i 16v – **May 1995**
No.12 Rover 1.6/2.0 EFi – **June 1995**
No.13 Rover 1.6/2.0 ignition – **July 1995**
No.14 Ford Zeta 16v – **August 1995**
No.15 VW 1.8 Digifant – **September 1995**
No.16 Honda Legend/Rover 800 – **October 1995**
No.17 Ford XR2i/RS Turbo – **November 1995**
No.18 Peugeot 405 Mi16 – **December 1995**
No.19 Renault Clio 1.2i – **January 1996**
No.20 Vauxhall 24v – **February 1996**
No.21 Range Rover V8 – **March 1996**
No.22 Honda Civic 1.6 – **April 1996**
No.23 Rover 820 single point – **May 1996**
No.24 Jaguar 3.6 straight six – **June 1996**
No.25 Audi 80 – **July 1996**
No.26 Ford Escort/Fiesta – **August 1996**
No.27 Vauxhall 1.8i – **September 1996**
No.28 Saab 900/9000 – **November 1996**
No.29 VW Digifant update – **December 1996**
No.30 Vauxhall Ecotec – **January 1997**
No.31 Nissan Micra 16V – **February 1997**
No.32 Peugeot 1.8i – **March 1997**

The Autodiagnos Multi Tester Plus provides unbeatable access to the Bosch LH 2.4 system used on this 2.0-litre Volvo application. Equipping yourself with this handset and the necessary software pod will cost about £3,000.

like this, within the closed-loop emission control system, require careful analysis if confusion is to be avoided.

There are several ways to check for air leaks. One is to temporarily plug the exhaust tailpipe and apply a soapy spray to the manifold area and watch for tell-tale bubbles. For best results do this with a cold engine because a hot one will evaporate the spray quicker than you can apply it!

Fuel pump failure is another relatively common Volvo problem, not only on this model but right across the range. The most likely cause is that the control relay, which is pulled down by the ECU (pin 20), fails to operate. Normally the problem lies not with the relay but with the ECU – not providing the switching action to earth. Unfortunately, this is nearly always

caused by internal circuit failure and there is no alternative but to replace the whole unit.

The good news is that faulty ECUs can be rebuilt and this is the best course of action. Refurbished units cost about £175, new ones about £350. Some less scrupulous garages have been tempted to re-wire the relay so that earth is

achieved along another path and the fuel pump runs continuously as long as the ignition is switched on. This is bad news from a safety point of view and is certainly not a solution that we would recommend.

BOSCH LH 2.4 JETRONIC

Drawing supplied by ATP Electronic Developments Ltd. Drawn by R. Keys.

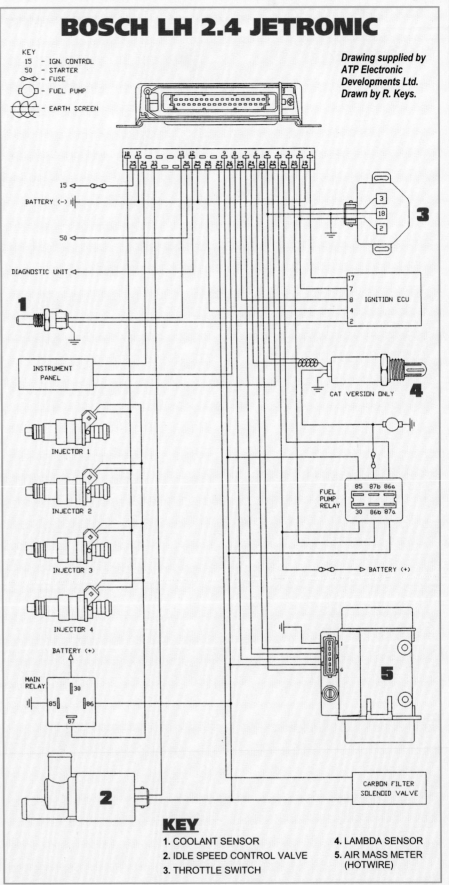

KEY
15 – IGN. CONTROL
50 – STARTER
◇◁▷ – FUSE
– FUEL PUMP
– EARTH SCREEN

KEY

1. COOLANT SENSOR
2. IDLE SPEED CONTROL VALVE
3. THROTTLE SWITCH
4. LAMBDA SENSOR
5. AIR MASS METER (HOTWIRE)

NEXT MONTH
BMW 5-series.

FOR ALL YOUR AIR FLOW METER AND ECU REQUIREMENTS, CONTACT YOUR NEAREST ATP STOCKIST.

ENGLAND

ATP SOUTH-WEST BRISTOL, AVON	TEL. No. 0117 9572997 FAX. No. 0117 9561290	
AUTO TECHNIQUE LTD LUTON, BEDFORDSHIRE	TEL. No. 01582 414000 FAX. No. 01582 419690	
AUTOCRAFT DUNSTABLE, BEDFORDSHIRE	TEL. No. 01582 866688 FAX. No. 01582 866618	
CAFCO AUTOMOTIVE LTD BOURNE END, BUCKINGHAMSHIRE	TEL. No. 01628 531181 FAX. No. 01628 528014	
CHARLTON RECYCLED AUTOPARTS WATERBEACH, CAMBRIDGESHIRE	TEL. No. 01223 863386 FAX. No. 01223 862555	
HUDSON MOTOR COMPANY JERSEY, CHANNEL ISLANDS	TEL. No. 01534 878847 FAX. No. 01534 89236	
CAMCO 88 WARRINGTON, CHESHIRE	TEL. No. 01925 445688 FAX. No. 01925 444988	
TEESSIDE AUTO TECHNICAL SERVICES THORNABY, CLEVELAND	TEL. No. 01642 617626 FAX. No. 01642 678610	
ALBASTON AUTO SPECIALIST LTD ALBASTON, CORNWALL	TEL. No. 01822 832514 FAX. No. 01822 833101	
MGM MOTORS CARLISLE, CUMBRIA	TEL. No. 01228 546079	
PEACOCK & PURVEY CHILWELL, DERBYSHIRE	TEL. No. 0115 9253639 FAX. No. 0115 9253639	
SCHILWARD MOTORS LTD CHELMSFORD, ESSEX	TEL. No. 01245 361383 FAX. No. 01245 362698	
SAMES LTD SOUTHEND-ON-SEA, ESSEX	TEL. No. 01702 344613 FAX. No. 01702 333723	
JR TRANSMISSIONS FARNBOROUGH, HAMPSHIRE	TEL. No. 01252 548337 FAX. No. 01252 370442	
STATION GARAGE SOUTHAMPTON, HAMPSHIRE	TEL. No. 01489 584567 FAX. No. 01489 583468	
HAMPSHIRE AUTO ELECTRICS LTD WINCHESTER, HAMPSHIRE	TEL. No. 01962 841010 FAX. No. 01962 840999	
TJS MOTORS STEVENAGE, HERTFORDSHIRE	TEL. No. 01438 356289 FAX. No. 01438 356289	
WATERLOO (MOTOR TRADE) LTD HULL, HUMBERSIDE	TEL. No. 01482 328416 FAX. No. 01482 212398	
THOMAS ELECTRO DIESELS ASHFORD, KENT	TEL. No. 01233 642816 FAX. No. 01233 647117	
BLACK BOX CHATHAM, KENT	TEL. No. 01634 405166 FAX. No. 01634 405166	
SWINFIELD-COOPER LEICESTER, LEICESTERSHIRE	TEL. No. 01162 545657 FAX. No. 01162 855653	
BROOME BROTHERS DAGENHAM, LONDON	TEL. No. 0181 599 2515 FAX. No. 0181 599 2516	
GL SERVICE GARAGE LEWISHAM, LONDON SE13	TEL. No. 0181 698 3475 FAX. No. 0181 695 9387	
SOUTHERN CARBS & INJECTION WIMBLEDON, LONDON SW19	TEL. No. 0181 540 2723 FAX. No. 0181 540 0857	
M & J PUMFORD WALLASEY, MERSEYSIDE	TEL. No. 0151 638 6060 FAX. No. 0151 638 0033	
MIDDLESEX TUNING CENTRE SOUTH HARROW, MIDDLESEX	TEL. No. 0181 422 3313 FAX. No. 0181 422 4664	
CLIVE ATTHOWE TUNING NORWICH, NORFOLK	TEL. No. 01603 702400	

LYNX SUPPLIES LTD BINGHAM, NOTTINGHAMSHIRE	TEL. No. 01949 836362 FAX. No. 01949 836628	
WR MOTORS SHREWSBURY, SHROPSHIRE	TEL. No. 01743 344618 FAX. No. 01743 344618	
R & D DONCASTER DONCASTER, SOUTH YORKSHIRE	TEL. No. 01302 323291 FAX. No. 01302 322169	
DJ ELECTRONICS MEAFORD, STAFFORDSHIRE	TEL. No. 01782 374131	
ANGLIA MOTOR PARTS LTD NEEDHAM MARKET, SUFFOLK	TEL. No. 01449 722618 FAX. No. 01449 722501	
AUTOMATIC GEARBOX CENTRE HOVE, SUSSEX	TEL. No. 01273 722155 FAX. No. 01273 722320	
BLUE LINE GARAGE SERVICES WALLSEND, TYNE & WEAR	TEL. No. 0191 263 8593	
MOTOR-RITE WARWICK, WARWICKSHIRE	TEL. No. 01926 410768 FAX. No. 01926 419086	
ASHTON ENGINEERING CO. LTD BIRMINGHAM, WEST MIDLANDS	TEL. No. 0121 643 5134 FAX. No. 0121 643 4212	
SOUTHERN CARBS & INJECTION CRAWLEY, WEST SUSSEX	TEL. No. 01293 529502 FAX. No. 01293 546570	
LOFTHOUSE INJECTION CENTRE WAKEFIELD, WEST YORKSHIRE	TEL. No. 01924 822247 FAX. No. 01924 870286	
AUTOELECTRO BRADFORD, WEST YORKSHIRE	TEL. No. 01274 656101 FAX. No. 01274 656622	
N.D HAIGH LTD HUDDERSFIELD, WEST YORKSHIRE	TEL. No. 01484 426479 FAX. No. 01484 513687	
KEITH LYE MOTORS MELKSHAM, WILTSHIRE	TEL. No. 01225 706796 FAX. No. 01225 791000	
FUEL PARTS UK BROMSGROVE, WORCESTER	TEL. No. 01527 835555 FAX. No. 01527 831111	
M.GOSLING ENGINE TUNING KIDDERMINSTER, WORCESTER	TEL. No. 01562 68427	

SCOTLAND

ES ALTERNATORS GLASGOW, STRATHCLYDE	TEL. No. 0141 776 3689 FAX. No. 0141 776 1115	
RETUNE ELECTRONICS GLASGOW, STRATHCLYDE	TEL. No. 0141 557 1414 FAX. No. 0141 557 2111	
ALASTAIR REID THE GARAGE GUILDTOWN, TAYSIDE	TEL. No. 01821 640368 FAX. No. 01821 640327	

WALES

AVW CAERNARFON, GWYNEDD	TEL. No. 01286 673559 FAX. No. 01286 676624	
PRATTS GARAGE CARDIFF, SOUTH GLAMORGAN	TEL. No. 01222 892347 FAX. No. 01222 891551	
JOHN ROBERTS MOTOR SERVICES WREXHAM, CLWYD	TEL. No. 01978 853882 FAX. No. 01978 853882	

KEY

– NETWORK 500 ECU TEST STATION

– ATP ELECTRONICS STOCKIST

ATP ELECTRONIC DEVELOPMENTS LTD
Unit 7 Hemlock Way, Hawkes Green
Cannock, Staffs WS11 2GF England
Tel: 01543 467466   Fax: 01543 467426

SUPPLIER OF THE LARGEST RANGE OF REMANUFACTURED AIR FLOW METERS, IGNITION, CARBURETTOR, FUEL INJECTION, ENGINE MANAGEMENT ELECTRONIC CONTROL UNITS, DISTRIBUTOR BLOCKS, FUEL PUMPS AND WARM-UP REGULATORS IN THE UK.

ELECTRONIC DIAGNOSTICS!

How to trace faults in electronic engine management systems

Number 34: Chris Graham samples the electronic manners of a Ferrari-red Fiat Punto 1.2-litre with single-point fuel injection.

This car relies on a Weber-Marelli 6F system for its engine management. It is found on both 1.1 and 1.2-litre-engined versions dating from around 1994 onwards and also, a little earlier, on the pint-sized Cinquecento 900. It is a single-point system and should not be confused with the alternative Weber-Marelli multipoint system used on other Fiat models.

In practice the two should be easily

TYPICAL FAULTS
1. **MAP sensor**
2. **Noisy tappets**
3. **Injector switching**

Car kindly supplied by:
Steve Moore, Caledonia Motor Group, Port Way, Ashton-on-Ribble, Preston PR2 2YQ, Tel: 01772 555800

distinguishable according to Frank Massey, the electronics wizard who

runs Preston-based Fuel Injection Services (Tel: 01772 201597). The single-point system has the old-fashioned appearance of a carburettor housing under an air cleaner assembly.

Frank's first impression of the system as a whole was encouraging. He knows of few serious problems and, although not a fan of single-point in any form, he has to admit that this Weber-Marelli set-up has proved pretty effective to date.

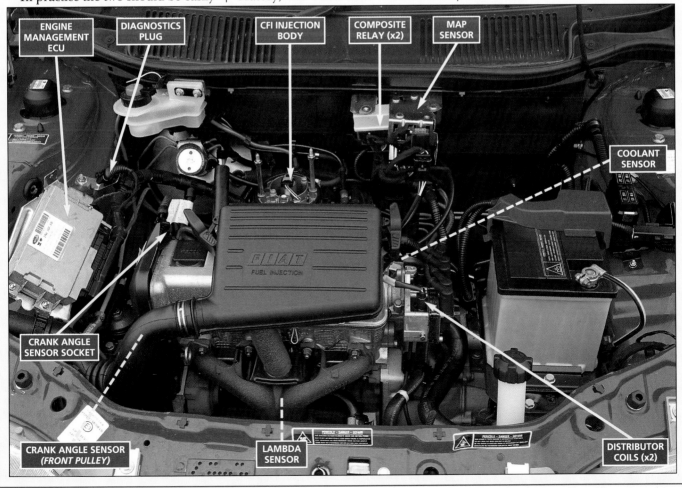

ENGINE MANAGEMENT ECU

DIAGNOSTICS PLUG

CFI INJECTION BODY

COMPOSITE RELAY (x2)

MAP SENSOR

COOLANT SENSOR

CRANK ANGLE SENSOR SOCKET

CRANK ANGLE SENSOR (FRONT PULLEY)

LAMBDA SENSOR

DISTRIBUTOR COILS (x2)

ENGINE MANAGEMENT

At the core of this Weber-Marelli system is a centrally-mounted fuel injector body housing the following: a throttle potentiometer, a single-point fuel injector, a fuel pressure regulator, an NTC ambient air temperature sensor and a 12V, ECU-controlled dual-winding stepper motor. The latter controls engine idle and features four pins – two ECU ground-controlled, two for supply – producing a straightforward square waveform.

Other important components consist of: a three-wire, analogue MAP sensor located on the n/s engine bulkhead with a sensing line which feeds directly to the engine side of the throttle disc; a standard NTC coolant sensor mounted in the water jacket on the right-hand side of the inlet manifold; a crank angle sensor with a screened lead and three-pin socket with a convenient connector right on top of the cam cover (this monitors speed and position and produces a dual wave output).

A zirconium oxide Lambda (oxygen) sensor found conveniently in the front of the exhaust downpipe; a dual relay mounted next to the MAP sensor on the bulkhead; a control fuse also mounted at the same place on the bulkhead; a 35-pin Weber-Marelli ECU found on the o/s inner wing; a three-pin diagnostic socket giving access to fault codes and serial data located next to the ECU.

The engine runs with a DIS ignition system which is very straightforward and features two independent coils with their own connectors. The coils fire two plugs simultaneously, one on the exhaust stroke and one on compression.

In terms of how the system works the operating sequence is as follows. When the ignition is switched on all the sensors are fed with a small voltage which acts as diagnostic check. Once cranking begins the important output from the crank angle sensor will trigger the ECU which in turn will switch the pump relay on and start to drive the ignition coils and injector. As soon as the engine fires the sensors will become active.

The fuel injector is frequency-controlled because, being single-point, it does not have to be timed to a particular cylinder event – it is delivering fuel under normal atmospheric conditions. Effectively, it runs like an electronically-controlled carburettor. As long as it supplies enough fuel, (and this is determined by inputs relating to engine speed, temperature and loading), it does not really matter precisely when it operates.

Interestingly, Frank found that the pulse width of this injector was very much shorter than he had previously encountered. From this he presumes that its flow rate is much greater. His conclusion is that the short switching action has been set by Fiat for reasons of critical fuel control.

He also noticed that the system appeared to have true over-run fuel cut-off – the injector is actually switched off during over-run – which is comparatively unusual on single-point systems. Normally single injectors are left on to guard against flat spots which can be a practical problem when the engine is suddenly accelerated again. He attributes this to the superior level of responsiveness in the system.

The fuel pump is mounted within the tank and sends fuel to the injector body-mounted pressure regulator. This is non-adjustable. Also, with regard to the fuel system, there is a purge canister for the fuel tank which is ECU-controlled. This normally becomes active under acceleration when emissions which have been stored in the charcoal canister are fed into the inlet manifold.

There is an inertia switch mounted on the floor of the car on the outside of the front passenger seat. In the event of an impact, this system will be tripped to shut down the fuel pump – resetting is simply a matter of pressing the button down again.

Finally there is an engine immobiliser system on the car which uses the increasingly common dual encryption control. The ignition key has a transponder which is programmed with a code that is read automatically as the ignition is switched on. If the two coincide then the engine can be started, if not, it will not run.

From new the car is supplied with three ignition keys – a master coloured red and two blue ones for everyday use. The red key can be used by the owner to re-encrypt the immobiliser if, for whatever reason, one of the blue ones defaults. However, if the red one is lost then we have been advised that a replacement costs £700! Frank believes that the reason for this great cost is that it comes with an encrypted ECU as well. So secondhand buyers beware! If no red master key is offered then knock £700 off the price or walk away.

Unfortunately, even if the red key is provided this does not mean it is correct – replacements are readily available but may not be correctly encrypted for the vehicle. To test, insert the key and switch on the ignition. A warning light on the dash (bottom left) will illuminate briefly and then go out. Switch off and then on a second time and the warning light should then remain lit. If it does not then the key is incorrectly encrypted.

Preparation

The sensible layout of the engine bay makes for easy access to all the important components.

The DIS coils are covered by a plastic cover which only protects them from the top – Frank thinks that dirt could work its way up from below. Consequently, it's well worth whipping it off and checking that everything is ship-shape underneath. All components should be clean, free from oil and grit and dry.

Remember that the DIS system is inherently powerful so Frank warns that any damage to HT leads will readily lead to tracking. The 'buzz' flying about could be anything up to 60kV so it's not to be meddled with. If this finds its way into a low voltage circuit then the potential is there for serious ECU damage, not to mention corrupted outputs possibly causing the ECU to engage limp home or fault codes.

Remove and check the condition and type of the spark plugs. Make sure that the colour of each is consistent – it should be, because of the single-point

configuration, but if it's not and all plugs are functioning correctly, then consider the problem to be valve-related.

Quite a common occurrence these days is 'sticky' valves caused by deposits of lacquer on them or the lifters themselves. Frank says that the use of a modern flushing additive can work

wonders for this condition and his understanding is that Fiat dealers make regular use of this type of treatment. With this in mind it makes sense, if you are looking at a higher mileage car, to flush the engine and change the oil before attempting any tuning work.

Check the vacuum pipe between the

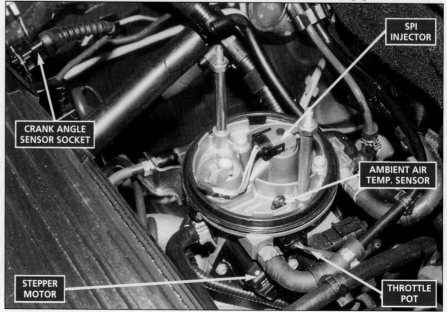

ELECTRONIC DIAGNOSTICS!

MAP sensor and the manifold. On this application it is a relatively short run, which is good, but there is still the risk of partial blockage from petrol or oil and of external damage, so inspect it's length carefully.

The wiring layout is generally neat, and Frank was unable to unearth any potential trouble spots. However, he points out that much of the wiring was cloth-bound and this inevitably attracts moisture and dirt eventually.

Sensibly, despite its apparently vulnerable location, the ECU is mounted at an angle to encourage water to run off and away from important connectors. Few problems should be encountered here.

Frank added that, although it is possible to remove the idle control stepper motor for cleaning, he does not advise it. His recommended approach is to apply carburettor cleaner down through the injector venturi and to leave it at that.

Finally, one other tip relates to the crankcase ventilation filter. Nowadays these are often ignored despite their important function. They are perhaps more significant now than ever before because of the closed-loop emission control systems being used. Any excess engine pressure caused by filter blockage will get fed straight back into the air intake, which is bad news for both the oxygen sensor and the cat.

Fighting the faults

Simple MAP sensor failure can lead to real trouble if allowed to go unchecked. If you come across a car with its engine management light illuminated then commonly this problem is likely to relate to one of two components – either the MAP or the Lambda sensor.

The MAP sensor is a simple device to check. Remember that it outputs a varying voltage, dependent upon pressure, so assessing its performance is simply a matter of connecting a vacuum gauge and a voltmeter. Range the pressure input and watch for changes in voltage output – they should not be hard to spot.

If no voltage variation can be detected then a new component is the only solution. Prepare for a bill of about £150.

Unfortunately, the problem can be a little more involved than this. Be on

Currently dealer-only diagnostic equipment is required to access fault codes and serial data but Sykes-Pickavant will shortly be launching a new Code Reader software pod for this system.

your guard because Frank has come across cases where replacing the MAP sensor appears to solve the problem, only then for the car to come back with the warning light shining again.

If there had been a problem with the oxygen sensor at the same time – quite possible due to excessive overfuelling – and its switching performance had not been thoroughly checked, then this could well have been hidden during the test drive.

The problem is that the oxygen sensor only codes itself when it is active. The component is over-ridden during aggressive driving – most garage test drives tend to be aggressive! – and so, because it is not operating, no fault is logged. But under a light-throttle driving style the sensor will be brought into action, at which point a defective switching action will trip the fault code.

Frank says that you miss this sort of fault at your peril because the cumulative effect can be a big bill. A new oxygen sensor costs about £110 and if the situation is bad then the cat may be shot too, adding a further £250 or so.

Also, linked in a way to the MAP sensor, there is a tendency for these engines to suffer with tappet problems. As we mentioned earlier, these can become noticeably rattly even when the car is still quite new. Engine flushing and an oil change is the best approach but Frank adds that often the car will have to be driven for upwards of an hour with the treatment in place before the problem is cleared.

The knock-on effect of a valve/tappet problem is that the engine will lose

TECHNICAL SPECIFICATIONS

(System 16F EG 1.2 55S Punto)

Injector	Cold	1.3m/s		
	Hot	0.55m/s		
	Acceleration	5.0m/s (blip throttle)		
	Crank cold	3.0ms		
	Frequency @ idle	1.5Khz		
Coolant Temperature Sensor	Cold	3.8V		
	Hot	0.6V		
Lambda Sensor	0.2-0.8V @ 2Hz hot			
Stepper Motor	12V to ground digitial		12V / 0V	
Crank Angle Sensor	2V static valve			
Crank Angle Sensor Signal			8V 12V	Offset 2V positive
Throttle Pot Switch	0.56V closed			
	4.3V Wot			
Map Sensor	Idle	1.5V	Supply	4.9V
	Overrun	0.6V	Earth	0.3V
	Static	4.6V		

THE SERIES SO FAR

No.1   Basic systems – **July 1994**
No.2   Diagnostic equipment – **August 1994**
No.3   Test preparation – **September 1994**
No.4   Ford 2.0i – **October 1994**
No.5   Rover 200/400 – **November 1994**
No.6   Vauxhall 2.0i – **December 1994**
No.7   Peugeot 205/309 GTi – **January 1995**
No.8   Ford 2.9i V6 – **February 1995**
No.9   BMW 1.8i – **March 1995**
No.10   Vauxhall 2.0i 16v – **April 1995**
No.11   Rover 2.0i 16v – **May 1995**
No.12   Rover 1.6/2.0 EFi – **June 1995**
No.13   Rover 1.6/2.0 ignition – **July 1995**
No.14   Ford Zeta 16v – **August 1995**
No.15   VW 1.8 Digifant – **September 1995**
No.16   Honda Legend/Rover 800 – **October 1995**
No.17   Ford XR2i/RS Turbo – **November 1995**
No.18   Peugeot 405 Mi16 – **December 1995**
No.19   Renault Clio 1.2i – **January 1996**
No.20   Vauxhall 24v – **February 1996**
No.21   Range Rover V8 – **March 1996**
No.22   Honda Civic 1.6 – **April 1996**
No.23   Rover 820 single point – **May 1996**
No.24   Jaguar 3.6 straight six – **June 1996**
No.25   Audi 80 – **July 1996**
No.26   Ford Escort/Fiesta – **August 1996**
No.27   Vauxhall 1.8i – **September 1996**
No.28   Saab 900/9000 – **November 1996**
No.29   VW Digifant update – **December 1996**
No.30   Vauxhall Ecotec – **January 1997**
No.31   Nissan Micra 16V – **February 1997**
No.32   Peugeot 1.8i – **March 1997**
No.33   Volvo 940 2-litre – **April 1997**

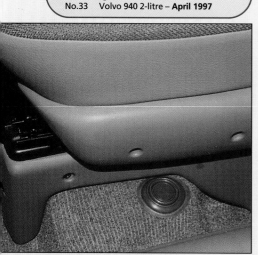

Everyone can find the inertia switch on the Fiat Punto!

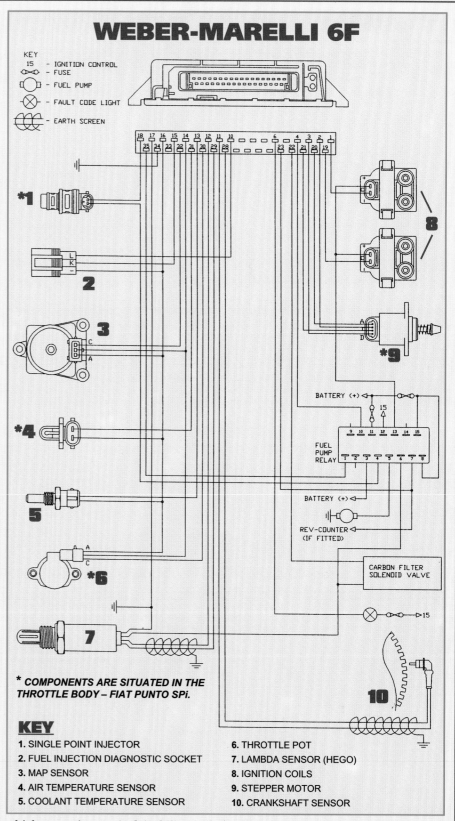

WEBER-MARELLI 6F

KEY
15 – IGNITION CONTROL
– FUSE
– FUEL PUMP
– FAULT CODE LIGHT
– EARTH SCREEN

* *COMPONENTS ARE SITUATED IN THE THROTTLE BODY – FIAT PUNTO SPi.*

KEY

1. SINGLE POINT INJECTOR
2. FUEL INJECTION DIAGNOSTIC SOCKET
3. MAP SENSOR
4. AIR TEMPERATURE SENSOR
5. COOLANT TEMPERATURE SENSOR
6. THROTTLE POT
7. LAMBDA SENSOR (HEGO)
8. IGNITION COILS
9. STEPPER MOTOR
10. CRANKSHAFT SENSOR

manifold vacuum and this, in turn, will cause the MAP sensor to adjust fuelling and instruct the ECU to deliver a richer mixture.

Consequently the car will over-fuel and, once again, the system will be heading off down the road towards premature oxygen sensor and catalytic converter failure. So be warned! What starts life as a relatively simple servicing problem can, with neglect, blossom into a serious and costly fault.

The final point worth mentioning relates to the fuel injector. As a rule, Frank says that single-point systems tend to suffer from injector contamination by lacquer from modern fuels. The result is that the injector's switching action becomes sluggish – it is slow at switching on and off.

'Lazy' switching inevitably leads to the production of a richer than normal mixture as well horrible flat spots which can ruin a car's drivability and send emission levels spiralling. The danger is that the over-fuelling condition will have a knock-on effect on the oxygen sensor and that the whole problem is blamed on this component.

One other possible cause is incorrect fuel pressure. Frank says this is unlikely but is always worth checking. The injector is the most likely cause, so remove it and send it away for professional ultrasonic cleaning and testing. They are simple and quick to remove. Once it has been cleaned and refitted, allow the oxygen sensor time to recover and check its switching again. This should be at a frequency of about two hertz and an amplinde of 500Mv-800Mv.

As far as the Fiat's injector is concerned, Frank considers that its exceptionally rapid switching action is likely to make the effects of contamination even more pronounced than ever.

NEXT MONTH
BMW 520 24V.

ELECTRONIC DIAGNOSTICS!

How to trace faults in electronic engine management systems

Number 35: Modern BMWs have a reputation for being complicated machines. Chris Graham investigates whether this is justified from a diagnostics point of view

The sporty, 24-valve straight-six variants of BMW's popular 3- and 5-Series saloons employ Bosch Motronic engine management. Essentially, this is Motronic M3 but, as Frank Massey of Preston-based Fuel Injection Services (Tel: 01772 201597) points out, this system is sub-divided into specific versions for specific applications – such as M3.1, M3.3 or M3.3.1.

These are all just variations on a software theme and Frank says the choice

TYPICAL FAULTS
1. **Engine misfires**
2. **Running rich**
3. **Intermittent cut-out**

Car kindly supplied by:
Derek Woodman Ltd, BMW Centre, Vicarage Lane, Blackpool, Lancs. SY4 4ND. Tel: 01253 697101.

essentially relates to vehicle specification. The presence of automatic transmission or variable cam timing are the types of feature which determine the

system specification. These forms of Bosch Motronic arrived on the three and 5-Series BMWs in about 1991 and are used on two and 2.5-litre cars.

Open the bonnet on one of these models and you will find a very 'cosmetically finished' engine. Plenty of plastic presenting a comfortingly simple appearance. The reality, beneath the moulded panels, is very different. Frank says that the system is complex and requires professional-quality equipment for successful remedial work.

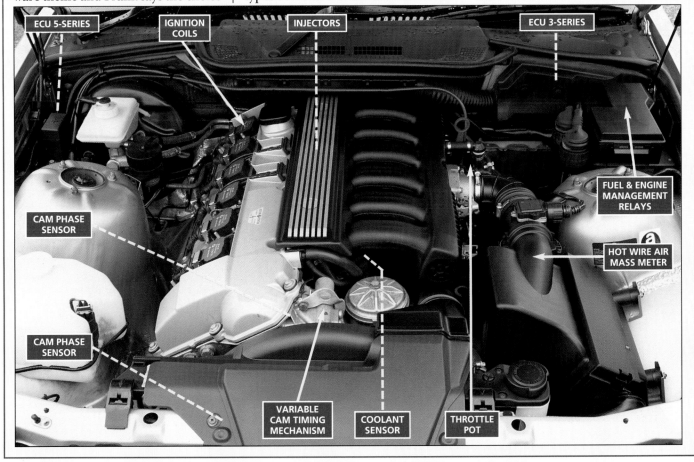

ECU 5-SERIES · IGNITION COILS · INJECTORS · ECU 3-SERIES · FUEL & ENGINE MANAGEMENT RELAYS · HOT WIRE AIR MASS METER · CAM PHASE SENSOR · CAM PHASE SENSOR · VARIABLE CAM TIMING MECHANISM · COOLANT SENSOR · THROTTLE POT

ENGINE MANAGEMENT

On the 5-Series the 88-pin ECU is easy to find and get at – it's located under a plastic cover against the bulkhead on the o/s of the engine bay. Things aren't as simple on the 3-Series because unfortunately the same ECU is found on the n/s of the engine bay, at the back and beneath a pop-riveted plate!

Fuel injection is sequential and for overall control the system relies on the following components: a crank angle sensor working off a phonic wheel on the front pulley; a camshaft phase sensor for identifying cylinder orientation for injection and ignition purposes and a standard NTC-type coolant sensor in the water jacket near the thermostat housing.

Also there is: a throttle potentiometer; an air mass meter; a rotary idle control valve; a conventional fuel rail; easy-access, multi-nozzle injectors; an in-tank fuel pump; and a pressure filter on the outlet circuit. All these are pretty straightforward components which we have come across many times before. Something more unusual is the Vanos variable cam timing facility fitted to some models. This is achieved by electro-hydraulic control and provides about 7 to 10° of valve timing variation – essentially to ensure a smooth torque curve.

The other really notable factor about this system, once some of the plastic covers have been removed, is the row of coils. There are six and each fits directly onto its own plug and is bolted into place. It is a very neat and tidy installation.

There is no HT wiring anywhere, which cuts out the risk of potentially disruptive RF radiation. Each coil is a conventional unit and has its own stand-alone wiring harness running directly from the ECU. All have a common supply, through the ignition switch, but dwell control is totally independent for each.

The ECU has six control pins, each of which will pull a coil down at the appropriate time, with reference to the crank angle and phase sensor input. The benefits of this are that the coil only has to be charged once to fire the cylinder so, in this example, it is working six times slower than a conventional component would have to.

A knock-on effect of this is that the coil windings can be much lighter, so they will charge much more quickly. These factors lead to a very efficient and high powered ignition system. From a diagnostics point of view they are simple to work with too – no rotor arm to worry about.

Frank has always argued that using an oscilloscope to look at coil primary performance is the quickest and most efficient way of assessing individual ignition quality. This signal will reflect the HT performance as a mirrored image – identical waveform.

No engine tuning adjustments are possible with this application.

His impression is that these types of installation are being designed with a view to deterring anyone apart from the dealer-based technician. They are difficult to get into, both physically and technically. All the wiring is engineered totally into the car, usually within sealed, plastic manifolds. The looms are very tightly fitted and often out of sight completely. Many of the leads are screened so they definitely cannot be cut into and the majority of sockets are very hard to get at.

The bottom line is that if you are not equipped with a good breakout box which will allow you to work directly from the ECU, or competent serial data test equipment, then you are sunk from a diagnostics point of view with these high performance BMWs.

In terms of overall reliability, Frank in not terribly impressed with the long-term performance of this system. It has built a reputation for blowing coils and, seeing as there are six of them, this is a problem! The nature of the set-up means that there is no scope for DIY investigation, certainly at the enthusiast end of the market. As we have said, the minimum requirement is for a breakout box but an oscilloscope really is a must, too.

You will be dealing with direct coil ignition – one coil per cylinder – which means that unless you have some sophisticated DIS equipment you will be struggling to pick up values even as basic as an rpm count.

However, there is hope. Frank says that diagnostic software from independent sources, is starting to become available. Autodiagnos already produce a pod for their test equipment and Sykes-Pickavant have one on the way for the Advanced Code Reader.

Nevertheless, without these aids, technicians must rely on pure diagnostic skills and their own ability to check and assess waveforms – there is no alternative. The task is not made any easier by the complexity of the ECU. It has 88 pins and a number of these have been made half the size of normal so back-probing needs to be an exacting and precise business.

All the primary sensors are well-concealed and Frank says: "God help you if you have to change even a simple sensor – they all involve a lot of work!"

Preparation

This can be a little involved with these 24V engines, although most generally remain very clean and oil-tight.

The air induction side is simple to deal with – between the air mass meter and the throttle body. Remove the air induction hose to get at the idle control valve. Remove this, wash it with carburettor cleaner, clean the throttle disc and check that the stop is correctly set and the throttle pot position is good.

Remove the spark plugs, which means removing the coils. Frank says that while it is not essential to keep them in the same order, it is good working practice to do so. It's always handy to be able to link a suspect plug with its appropriate coil.

Wash out the plug apertures then remove the rubberised extensions from the coils which are a friction fit. These are effectively the HT leads so must be treated carefully. Inspect thoroughly for age and heat-related splitting – if any are found, even small ones, the coil must be replaced. Unfortunately, rubber boots are not available separately and new coils costs about £80 each.

Gremlin grappling

Most problems with this 24V BMW application tend to relate to ignition, and perhaps the most common of all is an engine misfire. This will occur across the rev range, with the engine being very much down on power and displaying a 'lumpy' performance. The slightest sign of this must be regarded very seriously because this fault has the

AIR MASS METER

IDLE CONTROL VALVE

THROTTLE POT

ELECTRONIC DIAGNOSTICS!

potential to be very expensive.

Your first move should be to establish which cylinder is responsible for the problem; it will usually just be one. Pull back the rubber boot on each coil to expose the three wires. These are conveniently designated on the coil itself with numbers 15, 4a and 1. Number 15 is the ignition supply, 4a is a diagnostic link used by BMW to monitor coil performance and number 1 carries the ECU pull down control (dwell).

Use a scope to check dwell control on wire number 1 in each case to produce a 'traditional' coil primary waveform – refer to spec table. Assessing this will tell you a lot. The inductive spike will be clearly visible but its amplitude is important. It should rise to about 400V and if it does not then this can point towards a problem within the ECU.

After the initial spike the trace drops dramatically back down to between 30 and 40V and proceeds approximately horizontally, denoting the plug burn time. This 30-40V range is significant because it signifies that all is well with the 'HT' side of the coil – the rubber extension which attaches to the plug. Any resistance in this part of the circuit, due to cracking in the extension, will jack this voltage higher.

The burn time should be around 1.6-1.8ms, signified by the horizontal section of the trace. If it is shorter than this then the coil output is poor, leading directly to poor combustion and eventual catalyst and oxygen sensor problems.

Coil failure is relatively common and can occur instantly or progressively over a period of time. The bad news is that they can also fail drastically and invert into the ECU – they spike the primary windings with HT – which is curtains for the control unit.

New ECUs from BMW cost about £1,400 but refurbished units are also now available for about half this amount. There is an argument which suggests that once one coil fails, all the rest should be changed as a precaution against the same thing happening again.

Frank does not agree with this. He sees no reason for

The six coils exposed. Wiring is very neat and ignition system efficient but problems can be expensive. On the left is the diagnostic socket used by BMW dealers.

NEED TRAINING?

Frank Massey runs regular courses at his well-equipped Preston workshop. Everything from basic engine management introductions to full-blown 'hands on', system-specific tuition. **Call 01772 201597 for details.**

swapping the lot just because one fails. His experience suggests that there is usually an external reason for the component failure. For example, in a recent case he came across one which failed because it was actually cracked, probably by careless bolting down.

It should also be noted that the likelihood of premature coil failure can be highlighted by discrepancies in the primary waveform, even when no misfire is evident. Often poor burn time will point to this, together with a condition known as 'coil ringing'.

At the end of the burn time on the waveform there will be a short period of progressively diminishing oscillation in the trace. If this is not regular it can be another sign of trouble. This sort of work really highlights the worth of an oscilloscope. Using digital equipment to present the burn time purely as a figure severely restricts the information you can glean.

The overall message must be to deal with misfires promptly and effectively. Once faulty the coil may invert and seriously spike the ECU at any time. Even flat spots can be indicative of this developing condition. Ignore it at your peril.

A knock-on consequence of coil failure can be a rich mixture. Frank recalls a recent example on a car suffering with a misfire on one cylinder – poor spark burn time – although the relevant coil was still functioning. The confusing thing was that all six plugs showed signs of a rich mixture.

The owner had reported a

TECHNICAL SPECIFICATIONS

			ECU pin number
Fuel injectors	Hot	3.8ms	3/4/5 & 31/32/33
	Cold	4.5ms	
	Blip throttle	9.5ms	
Coolant sensor	Cold	3.7V	78
	Hot	1.0V	
Air temp sensor	3.0V @ 20°C		77
Throttle position switch	Closed	0.7V	12
	Open	4.4V	
Idle control valve	12V digital switch @ 100Hz 20% on @ idle		2/29
Crank angle sensor	30/20V peak to peak at idle 10V+ peak to peak cranking		67
Camshaft sensor	Single pulse, 30V peak to peak at idle		16
Air mass meter	2.5V at idle 4.8V snap load		41
Air mass meter burn off	3.5V for one second		13
Engine speed signal	10V digital, 40Hz at idle		74
Lambda sensor	0.2-0.8V at 1Hz+		70
Other useful references:			
Fuel pump relay pull down			1
Main relay pull down			27
5V power supply to all sensors			59

Coil Primary Waveform Assessment

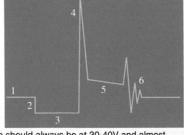

Working from the left: Ideally supply voltage **(1)** should be nominal battery voltage – 13-14V, followed by a clean, square switch **(2)** to ground. This should be held to ground during the dwell period **(3)** without interference. Induction or firing should have a vertical 'ping' line **(4)** up to 300V+. Trace returns rapidly down to burn line **(5)** which should always be at 30-40V and almost horizontal. Length should be about 1.6-1.8ms. Residual energy or 'coil ring' **(6)** should be even and without distortion before battery voltage is resumed.

THE SERIES SO FAR

BASIC SYSTEMS – July 1994 DIAGNOSTIC EQUIPMENT – August 1994 TEST PREPARATION – September 1994 FORD 2.0i – October 1994 ROVER 200/400 – November 1994 VAUXHALL 2.0i – December 1994 PEUGEOT 205/309 GTi – January 1995 FORD 2.9i V6 – February 1995 BMW 1.8i – March 1995 VAUXHALL 2.0i 16V – April 1995 ROVER 2.0i 16V – May 1995 ROVER 1.6/2.0 EFi – June 1995 ROVER 1.6/2.0 IGNITION – July 1995 FORD ZETA 16V – August 1995 VW 1.8 DIGIFANT – September 1995 HONDA LEGEND/ROVER 800 – October 1995 FORD XR2i/RS TURBO – November 1995 PEUGEOT 405 Mi16 – December 1995 RENAULT CLIO 1.2i – January 1996 VAUXHALL 24V – February 1996 RANGE ROVER V8 – March 1996 HONDA CIVIC 1.6 – April 1996 ROVER 820 SINGLE POINT – May 1996 JAGUAR 3.6 STRAIGHT SIX – June 1996 AUDI 80 – July 1996 FORD ESCORT/FIESTA – August 1996 VAUXHALL 1.8i – September 1996 SAAB 900/9000 – November 1996 VW DIGIFANT UPDATE – December 1996 VAUXHALL ECOTEC – January 1997 NISSAN MICRA 16V – February 1997 PEUGEOT 1.8i – March 1997 VOLVO 940 2.0 – April 1997 FIAT PUNTO 1.2 – May 1997.

definite backfire from under the bonnet, followed by an oily smell, after which the engine ran very badly. It lacked power and the exhaust emissions were sooty.

A new coil and a set of plugs were fitted but the engine remained rich. It would idle, but not well, and injection duration was virtually double what it should have been, pointing towards a potential sensor problem.

All were checked statically using a breakout box but no faults were found. Eventually he got the engine to run by shorting out the coolant sensor socket to give it a 'hot' value although the engine was cold. Then he discovered a very poor manifold vacuum caused by one of the breather pipes on the underside of the manifold having been blown off by the backfire.

This had created an enormous air leak so that the engine was drawing air from this source as well as the main induction system. The puzzling aspect was that, for some reason, a reduced air flow across the air mass meter was generating the richer mixture – perhaps due to a similar effect as acceleration enrichment.

However, once the breather was reconnected the engine ran as sweetly as ever. This problem highlighted the need for the technician to always keep things simple and constantly monitor the basics as well as the more technically involved aspects.

The other danger with continued use of a misfiring car is that it will quickly start to affect other expensive components in the system, notably the catalytic converter.

Cruising on the motorway at 4,000rpm with a misfire will rapidly damage the cat. Frank says that just a couple of minutes of this type of operation will deposit and ignite enough fuel on the core of the cat to do ir-

reparable damage. Around town this probably will not happen simply because the cat will not be hot enough.

The nightmare scenario is that a coil goes down on the motorway when the engine is hot and being driven at high speed. It could damage the ECU in a flash and trash the cat a couple of minutes later – possibly causing £2,000-worth of damage.

Another problem with great potential for confusion is a vehicle presenting intermittent engine cut-out. Suffering like this it may well start after excessive cranking and then could run perfectly until the random problem strikes again.

If you can 'catch' such a vehicle in 'no-run' condition then the tell-tale signs should be plain to see – no pulse to the coils, or the injectors and no relay pull-down to the fuel pump. All prime functions will be dead. At this point the problem could easily be diagnosed as

an ECU fault when, in fact, it is the factory-fitted alarm which is the root cause.

This problem is not one which we believe should be covered in a consumer magazine such as *Car Mechnaics*. Publishing information about the way in which the alarm defeats the ECU would simply make life easier than it already is for the reprobates in society who, apparently, steal a car every two seconds in the UK.

Finally, one other possible cause of ignition-related problems is a loose phonic wheel. This is a simple friction-fit on the front pulley and if it works loose and rotates it will alter the timing.

An engine exhibiting bad pinking, but not burning oil, could well be suffering in this way. Any play found (and it's usually detectable by hand) will necessitate a new front pulley.

NEXT MONTH
Citroën AX 1.0

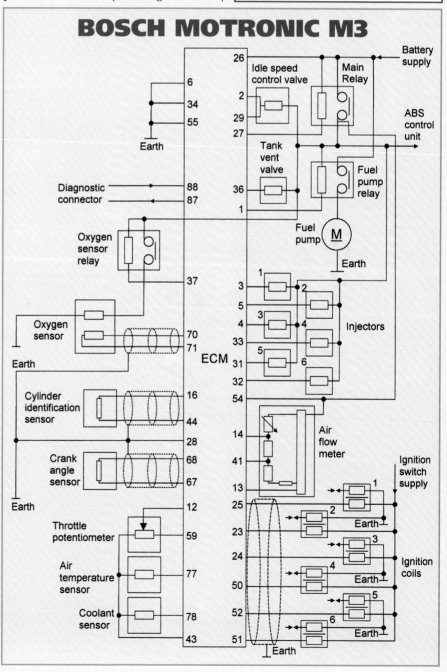

BOSCH MOTRONIC M3

ELECTRONIC DIAGNOSTICS!

How to trace faults in electronic engine management systems

Number 36: The popular Citroën AX runs a Bosch single-point injection system but is it reliable? Chris Graham finds out.

In common with other French vehicle applications, Citroën chop and change a lot with the management systems used on their vehicles. The AX range is no exception and so the first task is to establish exactly what you are dealing with.

The vehicle featured here was a brand new AX 1.0 with single-point fuel injection managed by Bosch MA 3.0. This same system can also be found on some ZX models but alternatives are possible, notably Bosch G6

which is very different, so you must be sure before you start.

Frank Massey, the brains behind Fuel Injection Services (Tel: 01772 201597) and our expert guide to all things electronic, is certainly no great fan of single-point systems. However, he will admit that this one is generally reliable and performs reasonably well, particularly when new and in good condition. Unfortunately, as time goes by problems do arise, and it is these which we are interested in here.

The system is controlled from a single ECU – fuelling and ignition both being directly driven from the control unit, there is no ignition module. The

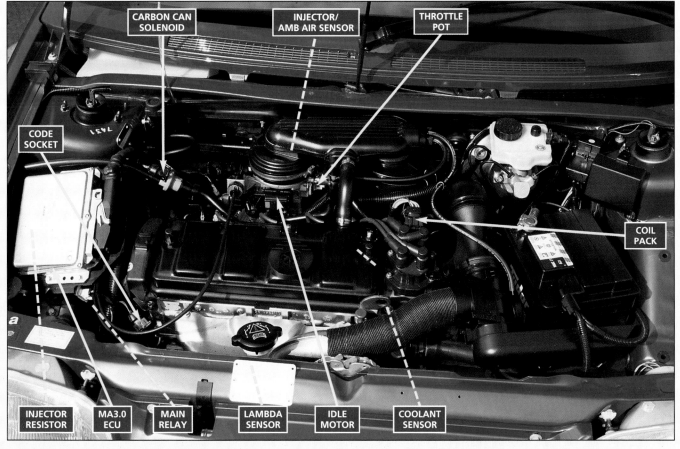

CARBON CAN SOLENOID · INJECTOR/AMB AIR SENSOR · THROTTLE POT · CODE SOCKET · COIL PACK · INJECTOR RESISTOR · MA3.0 ECU · MAIN RELAY · LAMBDA SENSOR · IDLE MOTOR · COOLANT SENSOR

73

ENGINE MANAGEMENT

This Bosch MA 3.0 system relies for its operation on primary inputs from just three components – the coolant sensor, a crank angle sensor and a dual throttle potentiometer. The latter is the more important because it governs the ignition advance and fuelling enrichment curves. Consequently, voltage outputs must be spot-on.

The throttle pots are assembled at the factory using a jig which holds the throttle disc in exactly the right position. Four security Torx screws are used to fasten the whole assembly together and supposedly make it tamper-proof – this is not the case.

The component is very sensitive to adjustment but Frank believes that there is no reason why an experienced technician, with a good voltmeter, should not make alterations when necessary. Bear in mind, however, that doing so will adjust the ignition and fuelling in very dramatic ways so it is important to get it right. If you are inexperienced and come across one that has evidently been tampered with, and the car is not fuelling properly, then the best plan is to seek some reliable advice before doing anything.

Within the main throttle housing there is the single-point fuel injector and a pressure regulator which is non-adjustable. On the side of the throttle body you will find the stepper motor assembly, which incorporates an idle on/off switch plus the drives to the motor itself which is a dual unit.

Other important components include: an ambient air sensor mounted close to the fuel injector; a stepping resistor which is mounted directly under the ECU and can be fitted either in the earth control circuit or the supply circuit to the injector; a composite main relay mounted on the inner chassis rail on the o/s near the suspension strut, effectively two in one, one half of which powers up the ECU when the ignition is switched on and the other pulls in the fuel pump and also powers components such as the Lambda sensor.

A Lambda sensor fitted in the downpipe of the exhaust and featuring a lengthy cable which runs round the back of the engine to a four-pin socket on top of the bell housing; a crank angle sensor which takes its input from a phonic wheel on the back of the flywheel (with 60 teeth, two of which are missing to identify TDC); a Hall effect road speed sensor incorporated into the speedo cable drive unit and located just outside the gearbox – produces eight outputs per revolution with a 5V square waveform.

There is also a charcoal canister so that vapour from the fuel tank is stored and recirculated through the engine under specific driving conditions – usually light throttle cruise or acceleration. The control valve is fitted just behind the engine on the o/s.

It should be noted that, in common with most other modern systems, all the socket 'boots' on this application are now made from moulded plastic and cannot be pulled clear for back-probing. Therefore a breakout box is essential and should be used – either a full-sized one at the ECU or smaller 'local' unit at the component. The other alternative is to back probe at the ECU but this can be difficult.

The engine runs on a DIS ignition system with a double-ended coil. This 'pack' is driven directly from the ECU (from pins 1 and 20).

ECU itself is a 55-pin component but only two thirds of the pins are used. Therefore, for diagnostic purposes an expensive 55-pin breakout box is required to do the job properly.

The system is code-readable via a green, two-pin socket found adjacent to the ECU on the o/s inner wing, beneath a black plastic cover. Using a code reader connected here provides access to fault codes – albeit a somewhat limited selection – and serial data.

PREPARATION

Once mileage starts to build on these vehicles problems can arise with the emissions recirculation system. Both the throttle disc and the injector can get contaminated and, in addition, the sockets around the injector body suffer with oil contamination.

There are three groups of sockets with four or five cables into each and it makes sense to disconnect all to wash out and dry thoroughly. You may also wish to add a quality electrical spray lubricant which will help prevent future problems of this sort.

Oil and dirt contamination may also affect the throttle pot internally and this must be dealt with carefully. We've already mentioned the critical nature of this component's setting and voltage output, so if you have to strip it be utterly sure that you mark the housing carefully. Use a scribe so that the unit can be re-assembled in exactly the same orientation. It's also a good idea to make an accurate note of the voltage and to ensure that this is re-achieved once you put the unit together again.

The DIS coil pack normally gives little trouble – Frank says that they are more or less dirt-tight. However, the HT leads can suffer from abuse so check them carefully. Any damage will necessitate replacement because the system runs at a high coil output so interference can be a problem if lead condition is impaired. Remove the plugs and assess their condition. Check the apertures and clean out thoroughly with carburettor cleaner when necessary.

Also bear in mind the tortuous routing of the Lambda sensor's lead. On this application this sensor generates a low voltage sine wave-type signal (0.2-0.8V). Unfortunately, the lead runs close to the alternator which produces a similar signal, but at a much greater amplitude, so there is the potential for electrical noise here – the cable length acts as an aerial!

In theory, the Lambda's lead is screened but Frank says he has yet to see one fully protected in this way. Interference from this source is more likely once the alternator starts to become worn and can be serious. It will affect Lambda sensor output to the ECU and lead to strange emission control faults. The only certain solution is to screen the lead effectively.

Finally, Frank advises that changing the engine oil and filter makes sense at the preparation stage, particularly on higher mileage examples. This is especially so if it is evident that the lubricant has not been changed for some time – ageing oil is likely to contain high concentrations of hydrocarbons

Labels: COIL LT TRIGGERS; NTC COOLANT SENSOR; LAMBDA SENSOR; CRANK ANGLE SENSOR/SOCKET; LAMBDA SOCKET

ELECTRONIC DIAGNOSTICS!

and/or petrol deposits which will detrimentally affect emissions.

PROBLEM SOLVING

Single-point systems always tend to suffer sooner or later with contamination of the injector and this leads directly to drivability problems including severe hesitation, flat response, stalling and/or surging.

Assuming that there are no other obvious causes such as an air leak, the most likely reason for such defects is a fouled injector. Lacquer liberated from the fuel builds up gradually to hinder the component's, mechanical operation. Because there is just one of them, the injector has to deliver enough fuel to satisfy all four cylinders so any interruption in its performance quickly leads to problems.

Frequently the consequence of contamination is that the injector gets 'lazy'. In practical terms this means that its switching action is slowed and becomes sluggish – often it will fail to close completely. The upshot of this is that more rather then less fuel is delivered and the mixture goes rich.

Dealing with this problem is not difficult and requires the removal of the

Sykes-Pickavant now have a software pod for this Citroën application.

injector so that it can be cleaned ultrasonically. Frank believes that this is the only certain way of shifting the contamination – he has not found the many and varied additive treatments totally successful. Once cleaned, the injector should deliver less fuel than before and engine response will become crisp once again.

It is possible that drivability problems will be flagged by a code relating to a Lambda sensor fault. However, never take this as the gospel truth and, as with all coded faults, think round the problem and consider other possible causes before taking action.

In this case, Frank says the best approach is always to check the injector first. Its failure will affect Lambda switching as a knock-on consequence and so can lead to the wrong repair

route being taken – the unnecessary fitting of a new sensor can be an expensive mistake!

Frank says that many engines nowadays suffer from poor fuel control. This can relate to Lambda sensor failure but also to a number of mechanical defects, including incorrect tappet clearances, air leaks, sticking valves or deficiencies in the manifold vacuum. All of these potential causes must be eliminated before the sensor itself is blamed.

Your first move should be to attach a vacuum gauge to the engine and confirm that the vacuum is good – 18-20in/Hg or better under ideal conditions. If this is not the case then consider factors such as camshaft timing, air leaks etc.

The simplest way to track down air leaks is by spraying soapy water around the manifold and watching for the tell-tale bubbles. Frank adds that if the vacuum is consistently low then the problem may well lie with the valve timing but if it is erratic then it is likely that a valve is sticking.

The primary key to the Lambda sensor's performance is its switching rate. Ideally this should occur at one hertz or better but when trouble strikes switching is slowed. The amplitude of the switch is important too. It must range from 0.2-0.8V. Observation of these two performance characteristics will tell all.

Frank explains that if the Lambda is switching slowly, but nevertheless throughout its full range, then the likelihood is that the sensor itself is at fault. Its action has become lazy which is a characteristic of an ageing component. The practical symptoms of this are that the engine will surge when being driven on light throttle – the fuel is being switched on and off slowly and causing

TECHNICAL SPECIFICATIONS

		ECU pin number
Ambient air sensor	2-3V	27
Coolant temp. sensor	2-3V cold 0.5-1V hot	25
Lambda sensor	200-800mV@1Hz+	28/10
Throttle pot (1)	0-24°, sensitivity ±0.1° Approx. 1V@idle 4.5V with open throttle	n/a
Throttle pot (2)	18-85° 0V@idle 4V with open throttle No output until 18°	n/a
Crank angle sensor signal	Sinewave composite 10V peak to peak speed 20V peak to peak TDC@idle Approx. 50% less during cranking	30/31
Injector duration	3-4ms cold 1.5-2.5ms hot 10-15ms snap load	
Idle control valve	0-12V digital Feed and earth switched dependent on motor travel	15+33
Idle switch	0V closed 12V open	2 (12V) 31 (ground path) (not adjustable)
Coil triggers	Digital 5V	1/20
Fuel pressure	0.8-1.2 bar	
Fuel flow rate	70lt/hr+	

THE SERIES SO FAR

BASIC SYSTEMS – July 1994 DIAGNOSTIC EQUIPMENT – August 1994 TEST PREPARATION – September 1994 FORD 2.0i – October 1994 ROVER 200/400 – November 1994 VAUXHALL 2.0i – December 1994 PEUGEOT 205/309 GTi – January 1995 FORD 2.9i V6 – February 1995 BMW 1.8i – March 1995 VAUXHALL 2.0i 16V – April 1995 ROVER 2.0i 16V – May 1995 ROVER 1.6/2.0 EFi – June 1995 ROVER 1.6/2.0 IGNITION – July 1995 FORD ZETA 16V – August 1995 VW 1.8 DIGIFANT – September 1995 HONDA LEGEND/ROVER 800 – October 1995 FORD XR2i/RS TURBO – November 1995 PEUGEOT 405 Mi16 – December 1995 RENAULT CLIO 1.2i – January 1996 VAUXHALL 24V – February 1996 RANGE ROVER V8 – March 1996 HONDA CIVIC 1.6 – April 1996 ROVER 820 SINGLE POINT – May 1996 JAGUAR 3.6 STRAIGHT SIX – June 1996 AUDI 80 – July 1996 FORD ESCORT/FIESTA – August 1996 VAUXHALL 1.8i – September 1996 SAAB 900/9000 – November 1996 VW DIGIFANT UPDATE – December 1996 VAUXHALL ECOTEC – January 1997 NISSAN MICRA 16V – February 1997 PEUGEOT 1.8i – March 1997 VOLVO 940 2.0 – April 1997 FIAT PUNTO 1.2 – May 1997 BMW 24V – June 1997.

the engine to respond accordingly.

A further consequence of slow switching is that the emissions at the tailpipe may well show a regular variation during the test. However, before you finally condemn the sensor remember that most nowadays have two earths, one for the heater and the other for the output. Both must be 0.2V or better and this is crucial.

If you find a Lambda sensor producing a fixed output and no switching action at all, then the sensor could well be fouled due to an incorrect fuel/air mixture. Use the appearance of the spark plugs as a practical guide to this. If they are the correct colour then the fault is with the sensor but black or white colouration – denoting rich or weak mixture – indicate that the Lambda is probably contaminated and therefore not working. The sensor can be cleaned if the deposits are not too bad but often it will be damaged beyond repair.

If you decide to change the Lambda then it is important that you then make sure that the engine is fuelling properly because a continuing state of poor engine tune will damage the new sensor. Remember, also, that the knock-on effect of this type of fuelling problem can be serious if not terminal damage to the catalytic converter.

Other mixture problems can relate to throttle pot. outputs. Both are crucial to the efficient running of the engine. They directly affect correct idle control response and overall fuelling so problems can present themselves as erratic idling performance or excessive fuel consumption. Unfortunately, Frank says that there is no official voltage data available for these pots although, measurements taken from a brand new vehicle can usually be regarded as being correct.

If adjustments are required, Frank's approach is to connect an oscilloscope

to the Lambda sensor and then to gradually rotate the potentiometer until the best switch (frequency and range) is achieved with the engine at cruise (3,000rpm). In this way you are measuring 'up stream' and not relying on the performance and efficiency of the cat. Then, with the engine at idle, repeat the test and if all is well then the body can be locked up finally.

However, Frank's cautionary advice is that if the pot has never before been altered, then it is probably not the cause of the trouble. Check its performance carefully first using an oscilloscope before doing anything drastic. Range the component completely and check both outputs. If these are electrically 'clean' then all is well. If not then stripping and cleaning must be considered, or even replacement.

One other possibility is wear on the

pot's tracks. These can cause 'noise' on the output voltage signal, in the same way that ageing air flow meters suffer. Upsets in the voltage output caused by this can be sufficient to throw the system into 'limp home' mode, resulting in flat performance.

Finally, failure of the road speed sensor can be another cause of erratic idle. The function of this component is to act as a trigger for different modes of throttle control, stepper motor and Lambda sensor operation – all factors which can be varied once the vehicle is on the move. Consequently, this is an important component and its output, which is sent to pin nine at the ECU, is always well worth checking. The signal is a digital, square wave.

NEXT MONTH
Nissan Primera

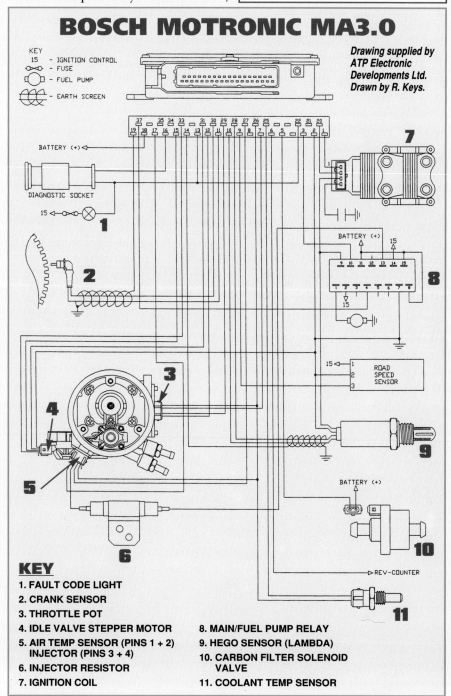

BOSCH MOTRONIC MA3.0

Drawing supplied by ATP Electronic Developments Ltd. Drawn by R. Keys.

KEY
15 – IGNITION CONTROL
– FUSE
– FUEL PUMP
– EARTH SCREEN

BATTERY (+)

DIAGNOSTIC SOCKET

BATTERY (+)

ROAD SPEED SENSOR

BATTERY (+)

REV-COUNTER

KEY

1. FAULT CODE LIGHT
2. CRANK SENSOR
3. THROTTLE POT
4. IDLE VALVE STEPPER MOTOR
5. AIR TEMP SENSOR (PINS 1 + 2) INJECTOR (PINS 3 + 4)
6. INJECTOR RESISTOR
7. IGNITION COIL
8. MAIN/FUEL PUMP RELAY
9. HEGO SENSOR (LAMBDA)
10. CARBON FILTER SOLENOID VALVE
11. COOLANT TEMP SENSOR

ELECTRONIC DIAGNOSTICS!

How to trace faults in electronic engine management systems

Number 37: Nissan's very popular Primera is a strong sales performer but what of its electronic manners? Chris Graham finds out.

The new 2.0-litre Primera featured here is fitted with the latest version of Nissan's own ECCS engine management system, incorporating multipoint fuel injection. Having arrived in the early 1980s, the ECCS system is well established now but started life as a fuel injection system only. Since then it has grown up into a complete and refined total engine management package.

According to Frank Massey, proprietor and driving force behind Preston-

TYPICAL FAULTS
1. **Rich mixture**
2. **EGR valve**
3. **Distributor drive**

Car supplied by:
Fred Coupe (Preston) Ltd, Chorley Road, Walton-le-Dale, Preston PR5 4JB.
Tel: 01772 253911

based Fuel Injection Services (Tel: 01772 201597), the most interesting and notable component on this system is the distributor, which contains a

number of unusual components including an optical signal generator. He believes this is a uniquely Japanese system and adds that it performs impressively well and accurately at denoting engine position and speed.

This most recent version of ECCS appeared in 1990 but doesn't have its own individual designation. Frank thinks that its introduction coincided with the adoption of catalytic converters, and adds that it can be found in varying forms right across the current

POWER STEERING SWITCH

FAST IDLE CONTROL VALVE (FICD) AUXILIARY AIR CONTROL (AAC)

THROTTLE POT

FUEL RAIL, PRESSURE REGULATOR 4x INJECTORS

CARBON CANISTER

COOLANT TEMPERATURE SENSOR

AIR MASS METER (HOT FILM)

MAIN RELAY LOCATION

LAMBDA SENSOR

COMPOSITE SIGNAL DISTRIBUTOR

ECU CENTRE CONSOLE *VEHICLE INTERIOR*

ENGINE MANAGEMENT

Although working in the traditional manner, this Primera's complex distributor also features a built in crank angle sensor and a coil – called, appropriately enough, 'coil in cap'. Therefore, there is no coil lead as such and the conventional rotor arm is supplied by a second contact within the cap.

In keeping with many of today's other modern systems, the primary inputs for this system are very traditional – engine speed and position, temperature and load. Temperature is monitored by a conventional NTC sensor at the back of the thermostat housing (voltage starts high then drops as temperature increases), load is interpreted by a hot film air mass meter with a bi-metallic strip (generally more robust than the older hot wire variety) while speed and position, as we've already mentioned, is taken care of optically within the distributor.

The system has four injectors and fuelling and ignition are controlled by a single ECU. It operates closed loop emission control, with a cat and oxygen sensor in the exhaust, so no mixture adjustments are possible.

There is a charcoal canister for absorbing fuel vapour from the tank, and often an exhaust gas recirculation system, although not on the car featured here.

There is a diagnostic socket inside the car (driver's footwell) so code readers can be used with the appropriate software. Alternatively, two pins in the same socket can be bridged – the two vary from model to model so be sure before acting – to display flashing fault codes on the dash. Finally, there will also often be an LED on the side of the main ECU for the same purpose.

There are actually only nine fault codes listed for this application but Frank says that, as with most modern Japanese applications, these ones are normally accurate and reliable.

Other important components to note include: a throttle potentiometer mounted, as always, on the end of the throttle spindle; an ambient air temperature sensor found within the air mass meter; a plunge-type idle control valve governed directly by the ECU; a supplementary idle control system controlled by a thermal sensor in the water jacket; a fuel filter on the n/s bulkhead; two important relays in the fuse box on the inner wing – one for the pump, the other for the ECU.

The car featured was fitted with a factory alarm system called 'NATS', which Frank takes to mean Nissan Anti Theft System. He believes this to be very similar to the system used by Ford (they call it PATS – passive anti theft system). It relies on a duel encryption system so the key contains half the code while the transponder in the lock barrel has the other half. When the two are brought together a signal is sent to a separate alarm ECU to disengage the immobilised circuits.

This is generally a competent alarm system and it acts on a number of fundamental circuits including those for the fuel pump, ignition primary and injector pulse.

Because of this high degree of immobilisation, it is always worth remembering the possibility of alarm faults if you come across a vehicle where these central functions are mysteriously missing.

Nissan range, be it single, dual or multipoint fuel injection. However, the basic principals are the same for all.

PREPARATION

Historically, Frank has found that Japanese cars are always very good in this respect. Engine bays never seem to get terribly dirty and the motors are generally oil-tight. They run cleanly as well, so there are very few problems with carbon deposits building up in the induction system. Normally the crankcase ventilation is routed directly into the air intake manifold, not through the throttle body, which greatly reduces the likelihood of contamination problems.

So the throttle body will normally be acceptably clean but it is always worth checking. Pull off the intake hose to inspect and wash with carburettor cleaner as necessary. Remove the idle control valve, check and clean if required.

The distributor cap is a traditional one, in as much as there are leads going from it to each plug. However, inside there are effectively two carbon brushes – one which sits in the centre of the coil, and one in the middle of the cap for the rotor arm. On occasions you may find limited deposits building up in here, so wash out carefully and blow clean and dry before re-fitting.

If the cap is damaged at all then it must be changed without question – HT leakage can be a problem if cap defects are ignored. The photo-electric diode within is very sensitive to stray voltage and any HT flash-over is almost certain to damage it. The same can apply if poor quality replacement caps are fitted. Always stick with o/e parts.

The coil is easily visible with the cap removed but shouldn't normally need to be cleaned because of its 'protected' location. Beneath the rotor arm is a steel cover which shelters the signal generator. This takes the form of a very thin steel disc cut with many slots to denote engine speed and position – in fact 360, one for each degree of rotation. These are very small and cut precisely by laser. Consequently, dust or dirt can cause real problems if it's allowed in. There are also four additional slots within, one for each cylinder, with one being larger than the others to denote TDC.

The triggering elements for this are an LED and a photo-electric diode and these can be cleared by gentle blowing with compressed air if needs be. Carburettor cleaning spray may also be used, assuming no residue is left after evaporation. Perhaps even more appropriate is the use of a genuine electrical contact cleaner, just to be on the safe side. Remember that any damage to this equipment will necessitate a complete new distributor at £300+.

The HT leads are well routed so do not normally cause problems. However, remove the plugs and inspect them. Keep them in the order they came out and check appearance for tell-tale signs of trouble. As with any other application, a white appearance on any of them can denote a partially blocked injector or a manifold air leak. Black finish can indicate a dribbling injector or even a compression or sticking valve problem. Plugs are very informative and can be checked by every-

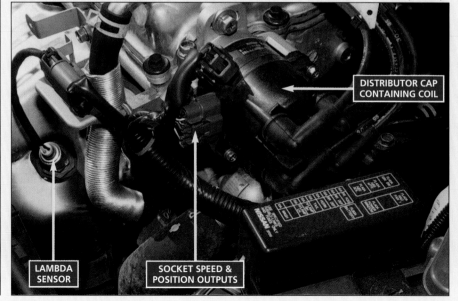

LAMBDA SENSOR

SOCKET SPEED & POSITION OUTPUTS

DISTRIBUTOR CAP CONTAINING COIL

ELECTRONIC DIAGNOSTICS!

one, so make use of this accessible 'window' into the inner working of the engine. If replacing, always fit the correct type, both in terms of heat range and resistive element and electrode style.

BUG BEATING

This car is equipped with closed loop emission control so there is both a catalytic converter and a four-wire, heated oxygen (Lambda) sensor. The system also has a 'limp home' facility which is activated upon the failure of certain primary components. This can lead to a strangely rich mixture which can prove inexplicable unless you know where to look!

When in 'limp home' the charcoal canister control valve is automatically opened so that the fumes from the petrol tank are being constantly drawn into the engine to produce a slightly rich mixture.

The problem comes because 'limp home' mode is actually very good on this vehicle. Many drivers remain unaware that the car has even reverted to it! So the car may well be entered for an MoT test only to fail with an over-rich mixture – HC emissions will be too high. Correspondingly, a check of Lambda sensor switching will show it probably switching at 0.8V which will confirm the richness of the mixture.

The unwary could be driven to

Alarm system on this Nissan is a dual encryption type. The key and the lock barrel work together to operate it.

changing the Lambda sensor or going on to check the fuel pressure and injection durations which will probably both be correct. The fact that it is drawing extra fuel through the carbon canister could mask the real fault.

In theory, the light on the dash should indicate an engine management fault and that the car has reverted to 'limp home'. However, there are several reasons why the warning bulb may not light – most commonly it could have blown or even been removed by an unscrupulous dealer!

So you are presented with a rich mixture for no apparent reason. Once the vehicle is out of 'limp home' the canister valve will re-set itself and all

will be well. The real causes could well be faults with the coolant sensor or the air mass meter but these get 'hidden'.

Alternatively, a wiring defect somewhere could be sufficient to trigger the change, even down to something as simple as a faulty electrical connector. It has been suggested that these cars are sensitive to under-bonnet pressure washing and that the connectors tend to be a little leaky, leading eventually to corrosion and problems. In this case the problem may even be intermittent, as electrical contacts kick in and out – even harder to track down!

Problems may also be encountered with the exhaust gas recirculation (EGR) system. Although not fitted to 'our' car, Frank says this is a common option on Nissans and explains that it does suffer with its own characteristic problems.

The idea of the concept is to lower combustion temperature. Exhaust gases are inert and although still hot, are actually far cooler than the temperature in the combustion chamber. By introducing them back into the system, usually only at high cruising speed, the temperature is lowered which helps to cut the production and emission of highly toxic NOx gases.

The most notable EGR problem is a sticking main valve. This important component is mounted within the exhaust manifold and allows a small proportion (approx 15%) of the waste gases to be re-introduced into the inlet manifold. Mostly these valves are controlled directly by the ECU, via a solenoid with vacuum pipe. Alternatively, the solenoid may be mounted directly on top of the EGR valve.

The soot and debris contained in exhaust gas can eventually cause the valve to stick and if it happens to lodge in the open position then problems arise. The most direct results are very poor idle performance, high HC emissions, a lower-than-normal manifold vacuum and a general reduction in engine power.

Although 'three-way cats' are now fitted to most vehicles which treat NOx emissions specifically (together with HC and CO), many manufacturers persist with EGR valves and so the risk of this problem remains a very real one. Once again, the condition can be misleading for the unwary.

If you carry out an inlet manifold vacuum check and find that it is lower

TECHNICAL SPECIFICATIONS

Crank angle sensor	Supply	5V
	Output	Digital frequency varying according to speed
Air mass meter	Supply	12V (NBV)
	Earth	0.25V
	Output	0.8V static, 1.4-1.9V at idle
		3-4V snap load.
Air temperature sensor	Output	5-7V at 20°C (loacted inside AMM)
Coolant sensor (NTC)	Supply	5V
	Output	3V cold, 1V hot
		Open circuit reference voltage 4.8-5V
Throttle pot	Supply	5V
	Earth	0.25V
	Output	0.52-0.62 closed
		approx 4V fully open
Injection duration	Cold	4ms
	Hot	2.5-3ms
	Snap	15ms
	Cold cranking	8-10ms
Lambda sensor	Supply	12V (heated)
	Earth	0.25V
	Output	200-800mV switch @ 1Hz+
Fuel pressure	2.8bar with vacuum	
	3.0bar without vacuum	
Fuel flow	60+ litres/hour, on return circuit	

THE SERIES SO FAR

BASIC SYSTEMS – July 1994 DIAGNOSTIC EQUIPMENT – August 1994 TEST PREPARATION – September 1994 FORD 2.0i – October 1994 ROVER 200/400 – November 1994 VAUXHALL 2.0i – December 1994 PEUGEOT 205/309 GTi – January 1995 FORD 2.9i V6 – February 1995 BMW 1.8i – March 1995 VAUXHALL 2.0i 16V – April 1995 ROVER 2.0i 16V – May 1995 ROVER 1.6/2.0 EFi – June 1995 ROVER 1.6/2.0 IGNITION – July 1995 FORD ZETA 16V – August 1995 VW 1.8 DIGIFANT – September 1995 HONDA LEGEND/ROVER 800 – October 1995 FORD XR2i/RS TURBO – November 1995 PEUGEOT 405 Mi16 – December 1995 RENAULT CLIO 1.2i – January 1996 VAUXHALL 24V – February 1996 RANGE ROVER V8 – March 1996 HONDA CIVIC 1.6 – April 1996 ROVER 820 SINGLE POINT – May 1996 JAGUAR 3.6 STRAIGHT SIX – June 1996 AUDI 80 – July 1996 FORD ESCORT/FIESTA – August 1996 VAUXHALL 1.8i – September 1996 SAAB 900/9000 – November 1996 VW DIGIFANT UPDATE – December 1996 VAUXHALL ECOTEC – January 1997 NISSAN MICRA 16V – February 1997 PEUGEOT 1.8i – March 1997 VOLVO 940 2.0 – April 1997 FIAT PUNTO 1.2 – May 1997 BMW 24V – June 1997 CITROEN AX – July 1997.

than expected (less than 22in/Hg), you could conclude that there was an air leak, perhaps a camshaft timing error or even a valve fault. The real culprit, of course, is the EGR valve.

If the car is fitted with EGR and you are doubtful about its performance, disconnect the valve. Usually there is a pipe connecting the valve to the inlet manifold, so remove this and blank it off. The system does not normally work at idle anyway, so if there's an improvement in manifold vacuum after doing this, you know the EGR valve is stuck open.

In keeping with most self-coding systems, the code which may be thrown up to highlight a problem should never be taken as the absolute cause of the trouble. On any application like this, when the primary trigger is built into the distributor, basic distributor problems can generate spurious faults.

For example, if the drive belt or chain breaks and the distributor stops rotating, the code triggered is likely to be failed crank angle sensor. If you were to proceed and check the signal from this component there would be nothing, further 'confirming' the diagnosis.

Going one stage further and checking for power at the main ECU, or even that the alarm was not at the root of the problem, would do nothing to dispel the initial diagnosis either. The simplest check, of course, is to remove the cap and make sure that the rotor arm is moving. So before formulating involved fault theories, check the basics.

In the worst cases you may even come across an engine which runs but shows an ignition timing error. Most data books now don't provide ignition values (simply saying 'computer controlled'), but Frank says that most engines now run at between 10-20° of advance at idle.

Bad belt replacement or tensioning can be to blame for this sort of trouble. Slackness may allow it to jump a tooth or two. In the case of this Primera

there is normally very little capacity for rotating the distributor body – just a few degrees of adjustment is available. So putting right a big deviation in this way is out of the question. Always check the pure mechanics of a mystery engine first. It makes sense and could save a lot of time.

Finally, remember that battery voltage and the general condition of the battery are crucial on this application – as they are with most modern systems. Frank says that most now have voltage compensation error within the circuitry to allow for normal, everyday fluctuations (under cranking and charging etc).

However, if the battery has an actual defect then the management system will recognise a poor supply and will compensate for it – sometimes by enriching the mixture or switching to 'limp home' mode. Don't be fooled. There are many components, including the injectors, idle control valve, EGR valve and the coil itself, which demand high current levels from the battery, and the performance of these is affected if the supply falls away. Some may be driven for longer to compensate. There is a threshold below which the system will crash.

NEXT MONTH
Renault Laguna

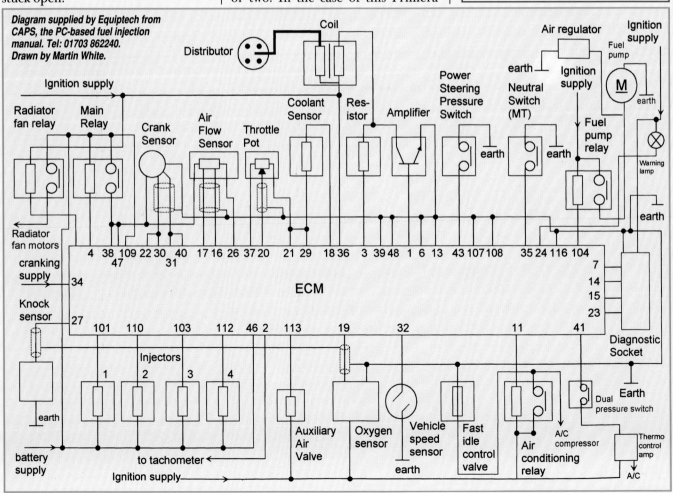

Diagram supplied by Equiptech from CAPS, the PC-based fuel injection manual. Tel: 01703 862240. Drawn by Martin White.

ic Now we offer the largest range of exchange ECUs and Airflow Meters in the UK.

Not only do Webcon have the ultimate range, but also the in-depth technical expertise to back it up. For virtually every make of car.

We can deliver our exchange ECUs and airflow meters overnight. Orders received before 5pm will be delivered a.m. the next day. Own unit repairs are handled and returned within 24 hours. Alternatively we have more than 300 outlets who in many cases can supply you from stock.

This typifies the total Webcon offer...the most comprehensive range of service components for all kinds of fuel systems. And that includes injectors, carburettors, air filters, fuel pumps, turbo-chargers and associated parts.

For further details, contact the Sales Department on 01932 787100.

WEBCON

WEBCON U.K. LIMITED, Dolphin Road, Sunbury-on-Thames, Middlesex TW16 7HE. Fax: 01932 782725.
E-mail: sales@webcon.co.uk Web-site on: http://www.webcon.co.uk

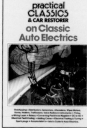

ELECTRONIC DIAGNOSTICS!

How to trace faults in electronic engine management systems

Number 38: Renault's Laguna 2.0 is a popular seller, but what about its workshop manners? Chris Graham unearths the electrical truth.

The two-litre Renault Laguna variant is fitted with the Renix/Bendix R engine management system featuring multipoint fuel injection. This is a commonly used control package across the current Renault range and, indeed, the 1.8-litre Laguna is a recent convert to this MPI set-up – previously it was a rather asthmatic single point.

According to Frank Massey, our resident automotive electronics expert and proprietor of tuning specialists Fuel In-

TYPICAL FAULTS
1. **Coolant sensor**
2. **Flat spots**
3. **Wiring problems**

Car supplied by:
Rogers Renault, Rogers Corner,
274 Fylde Road, Preston, Lancs PR2 2NJ
(Tel: 01772 722482).

jection Services (Tel: 01772 201597) this current system arrived in 1994 but there are some important distinctions to be made between the models.

Sensor type varies in a number of cases and appears to be determined essentially by engine number. Therefore, it is vital to identify exactly the vehicle you are working on, especially if replacement parts are required.

Refer to the technical specifications table for further information. Refitting the wrong coolant sensor, for example, will cause instant over/under-fuelling problems even though each of the component options looks identical. There is plenty of scope for confusion,

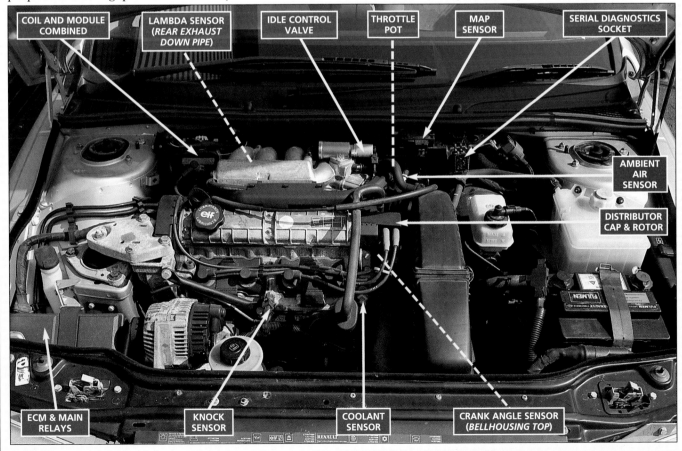

COIL AND MODULE COMBINED — LAMBDA SENSOR (*REAR EXHAUST DOWN PIPE*) — IDLE CONTROL VALVE — THROTTLE POT — MAP SENSOR — SERIAL DIAGNOSTICS SOCKET — AMBIENT AIR SENSOR — DISTRIBUTOR CAP & ROTOR — ECM & MAIN RELAYS — KNOCK SENSOR — COOLANT SENSOR — CRANK ANGLE SENSOR (*BELLHOUSING TOP*)

ENGINE MANAGEMENT

This Renix/Bendix system is essentially straightforward, with one injector per cylinder. It does feature knock control, consisting of a pezio ceramic sensor which is bolted to the top of the block with the objective of detecting pinking. Should pre-ignition be registered then a signal is sent directly to the ECU and ignition timing is retarded accordingly.

Other important components include: an air temperature sensor located in the air intake trunking; a coolant temperature sensor in the head; a throttle position indicator mounted on the throttle spindle; an external MAP sensor with pipe connected to the inlet manifold; and oxygen sensor; a catalytic converter; fuel pump and ECU main relays, both within the plastic housing containing the ECU in the front o/s corner of the engine bay.

There are also four injectors mounted in a common fuel rail and controlled by a pressure regulator, a fuel pump mounted internally within the pump, a pressure filter in the fuel supply line, a charcoal canister for absorbing HC emissions from the fuel tank with a solenoid control for releasing them back into the engine under certain conditions – usually acceleration and a plunge-type idle control valve (Hitachi).

Finally you will find a coil pack on the bulkhead consisting of a module and a coil controlled directly by the ECU, an inductive pick-up crank angle sensor which is the fundamental trigger for the whole system (engine speed and position data) and is at the back of the bell housing, a road speed sensor mounted on the transmission and a diagnostic socket.

There are reasonably capable self-diagnostic and serial communication prospects with this system and Sykes-Pickavant have available a Code Reader software pod specifically for this application. However, no tuning adjustments are possible so if something is wrong with this car it has to be a wiring, sensor or mechanical fault.

Electrical faults are indicated by a warning lamp on the dash. the early systems can only record current faults but later versions will store intermittent ones as well for retrieval by suitable testing equipment.

so be warned.

Overall, Frank was impressed by the underbonnet layout. The trend today is to bury important components out of sight, but this was not the case here.

PREPARATION

Fortunately, there is not too much to worry about on this engine application. Your first port of call ought to be the idle control valve. Because this is a plunge-type unit it must be kept clean and in good working order. Remove the unit and clean the two ports within using carburettor cleaner. Agitation with a bristle brush adds to the effect but the ultimate is to give it a 'rattle' in an ultrasonic cleaning bath. Moisten the shaft and seal before refitting.

On the whole the air induction side of this engine remains reasonably clean, however, it is worth checking anyway. Remove the main air hose and check/wash the throttle disc as necessary. Even small carbon deposits on the disc will be enough to affect the air flow at low engine speeds and so idle control can be upset in this way.

Also make sure that the throttle linkage has not been fiddle with, and likewise the throttle stop. Check as well that the cable tension is correct. Remember that any stiffness (lack of lubrication) or wear in the mechanical throttle linkage will affect drivability. If in any doubt, wash the whole assembly, re-lubricate and make sure that it operates smoothly through its entire range of movement. Really, this should be checked from the pedal to make the exercise realistic – a rucked-up carpet can be a simple cause of problems!

The ignition side is straightforward with a traditional distributor with cap and rotor arm. Unfortunately, the location is not all it might be, so road dirt contamination can be a cause of trouble. Remove the cap, wash out thoroughly and blow it dry. Do the same for the leads and check that the plugs are correct too.

Because the system is multipoint, fuelling should be consistent across all four cylinders, so any anomalies in plug appearance should be treated with suspicion.

Pay particular attention to the condition of the vacuum line running between the MAP sensor and the induction manifold. The integrity of this tube is vital to the system. Remove the pipe at the sensor end, wash down it with carburettor cleaner so that you are washing into the manifold too – carbon build-up here can be a potential source of trouble too.

Finally, with the pipe completely removed, gently blow through it to make doubly sure it is clear. Do blow gently, however, because Renault tend to use an air restrictor in this pipe (to reduce the pulsing effect from the engine to stabilise the MAP sensor's output voltage). Blowing too hard is likely to propel the said widget across the workshop and more than likely into oblivion!

PROBLEM SOLVING

Internal corrosion within the engine can be a problem with this Renault application. The manufacturers blame owners who fail to use the correct Renault coolant additive. Frank does not accept this explanation and is not aware of other engines which suffer in quite the same way, despite being made of the same materials and suffering similar 'abuse' from owners.

The most common upshot of this unfortunate condition is that the coolant sensor, which sits within the water jacket, becomes corroded too. This can be premature and aggressive in the worst cases.

The outer protective jacket of the sensor is eaten away to expose the active elements within. This obviously leads to eventual failure of the sensor which, in turn, can send the system into default.

In the early stages the problem can be intermittent. Frank has come across sensors with outputs which have been drifting slightly out of range. Not

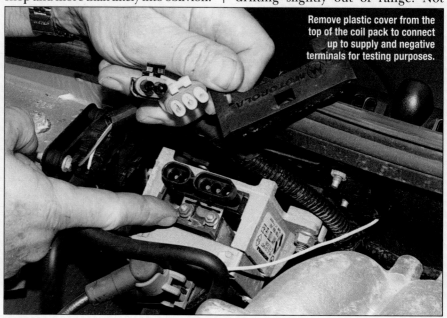

Remove plastic cover from the top of the coil pack to connect up to supply and negative terminals for testing purposes.

ELECTRONIC DIAGNOSTICS!

enough to cause a failure or arouse any real alarm but he knows now that this is the first sign of premature sensor failure caused by corrosion. One of the first practical signs can be poor starting performance.

The problem is complicated by the fact that, on this application, Renault actually make use of three types of coolant sensor! There are two types of conventional NTC sensor, where the output voltage starts high and then decreases as temperature rises. But there is also a PTC version which operates in the reverse manner – output starts low and rises with temperature.

The PTC and NTC types operate at slightly different voltage ranges (see table) and so are definitely not interchangeable. Fitting the wrong one is certain to confuse the ECU and cause all sorts of engine running problems. So if you come across a Laguna which is running badly and had obviously had a new coolant sensor fitted, check the type carefully.

All three look identical and it is only by relating the component part number to that of the engine that you can be sure of the correct application.

The Laguna has developed a bit of a reputation for flat spots. Quite often the engine management software is blamed for this type of complaint and, indeed, this can sometimes be the case. However, in Frank's considerable experience, a much simpler cause is incorrect fuelling. The most common cause of this is fuel injector fouling, but another prime reason can be inaccurate inputs from any one of several sensors around the engine.

In most cases, and this relates to all cars, not just Renaults, Frank is able to cure the problem by pure diagnostics. Assessing vital factors such as lambda sensor switching, MAP sensor voltage output, the quality of injector performance and fuel pressure, normally provide the answer.

Slight deviations away from standard specification with any of these will

Main ECU housed in two-piece plastic case on front o/s. On the nearside, just ahead of the battery, is the ECM for the ABS. This has no protection and ours was already showing signs of surface contamination. Trouble for the future?

be sufficient to cause noticeable flat spots and poor driveability problems. Frank understands that the official solution to these types of driveability problem is for the ECU to be swapped on an exchange basis.

However, he considers that this simply masks the problem rather than curing it at source – the new software simply allows more fuel to be pumped in! His approach is to change the ECU only as a last resort, once everything else has been checked and assessed properly. This approach usually avoids a lot of extra expense for the customer!

A different type of electrical problem relates to the way that Renault wire the Laguna. The risk is that some wires are vulnerable to water ingress, especially at points in the main harness where secondary circuits branch off.

Frank believes that Renault use two types of wire crimping to secure joints at these points, neither of which he is particularly impressed with. The first makes use of a solderless metal ring which simply encircles the contacts being joined. These can be a problem in the case of sensor supply and earth wires, which are often shared circuits.

A lack of voltage or earth on one of these circuits should alert you to the possibility of an internal wiring problem in the loom. The connection will have to be tracked down and exposed and, more often than not, corrosion will be the evident cause. This is a time-consuming and irritating business but it is not confined to Renault – Ford use a similar system!

A more modern jointing alternative recently introduced is potentially even more worrying for the long term. Basically, a tool is used to exert enormous pressure on the copper wiring so that the

TECHNICAL SPECIFICATIONS

Crank angle sensor	ECU pins 11 output and 28 earth	
	Output (crank)	2V peak to peak AC 0.7V RMS
	Output (idle)	8V+ peak to peak 3.5V+ RMS
	Output (3,000)	10V+ peak to peak 5V+ RMS
Knock sensor	ECU pins 31 output and 32 earth Active – tap block Output 1-2V AC @ 15KHz	
Air temp. sensor	ECU pins 14 output and 32 earth Reference voltage of 5V on both	
Water temp. sensor	ECU pins 15 output and 32 earth PTC type 0.6-0.8V@20°C, 1.0-1.2V@80°C NTC type 1.5-2.2V@20°C, 0.1-0.2V@80°C	
MAP sensor	ECU pins 33 output and 17/16 earth and supply Output 4.5V at atmosphere 3.8V at 0.2bar 1.6V at 0.6bar 0.5V at 0.8bar (idle 1.7bar)	
Oxygen sensor	ECU pin 35 output Output 0.2-0.8V @ 1-3Hz	
Throttle position Ind.	ECU pins 9 output, 17/16 supply and earth Output 0.5V closed 4.5V with throttle open	
Fuel injectors	ECU pins 21&22 feed fuel pump relay Inj duration 4-6ms cold 2.2-2.5ms hot 8-12ms cold cranking	
Idle control valve	ECU pin 24 feed fuel pump relay Signal is a 'saw tooth' RMS voltage of approx 8V	

THE SERIES SO FAR

BASIC SYSTEMS – July 1994 DIAGNOSTIC EQUIPMENT – August 1994 TEST PREPARATION – September 1994 FORD 2.0i – October 1994 ROVER 200/400 – November 1994 VAUXHALL 2.0i – December 1994 PEUGEOT 205/309 GTi – January 1995 FORD 2.9i V6 – February 1995 BMW 1.8i – March 1995 VAUXHALL 2.0i 16V – April 1995 ROVER 2.0i 16V – May 1995 ROVER 1.6/2.0 EFi – June 1995 ROVER 1.6/2.0 IGNITION – July 1995 FORD ZETA 16V – August 1995 VW 1.8 DIGIFANT – September 1995 HONDA LEGEND/ROVER 800 – October 1995 FORD XR2i/RS TURBO – November 1995 PEUGEOT 405 Mi16 – December 1995 RENAULT CLIO 1.2i – January 1996 VAUXHALL 24V – February 1996 RANGE ROVER V8 – March 1996 HONDA CIVIC 1.6 – April 1996 ROVER 820 SINGLE POINT – May 1996 JAGUAR 3.6 STRAIGHT SIX – June 1996 AUDI 80 – July 1996 FORD ESCORT/FIESTA – August 1996 VAUXHALL 1.8i – September 1996 SAAB 900/9000 – November 1996 VW DIGIFANT UPDATE – December 1996 VAUXHALL ECOTEC – January 1997 NISSAN MICRA 16V – February 1997 PEUGEOT 1.8i – March 1997 VOLVO 940 2.0 – April 1997 FIAT PUNTO 1.2 – May 1997 BMW 24V – June 1997 CITROEN AX – July 1997 NISSAN PRIMERA – August 1997.

strands being joined are literally crushed together into a small cube. After this has been done the whole lot is coated in plastic sealant but Frank has his doubts about the longevity of such a system.

He adds that if such a joint does become corroded it can cause real problems because the affected length has to be removed and then, of course, the two ends cannot be simply rejoined because there is never usually enough slack, so an extension has to be added, which complicates matters greatly.

Frank has also heard of a number of cases where Lagunas have suffered with badly corroded main earth strap. This can be severe in some cases but the causes are not clear. Possibly the condition might relate to inappropriate pre-delivery storage of the vehicle, or an exceptionally aggressive type of use.

Whatever the case, if you find a vehicle suffering with a poor earth then go right back to basics. Check the battery, the main earth strap and the earth strap to the engine. Corroded straps must obviously be replaced.

Lastly, the alarm system employed on this Renault warrants a mention – it's an interesting one with a strange peculiarity. From new the car is supplied with two ignition keys. These operate the dual key encryption mechanism so that a code within the key is paired with one stored in the ECU, and once the two recognise each other the vehicle can be started.

However, the curious aspect of the system is that each of the two keys can only be used to operate the alarm up to

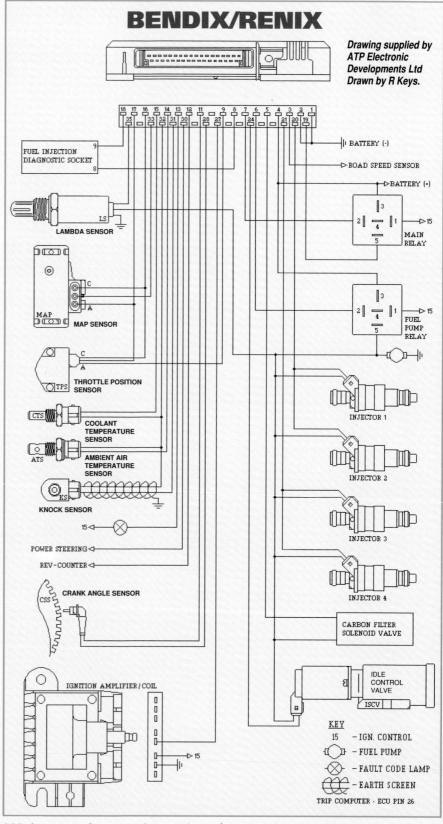

BENDIX/RENIX

Drawing supplied by ATP Electronic Developments Ltd Drawn by R Keys.

999 times (not that many in practice). Try for the one thousandth opening with the same key and nothing will happen – the alarm will not be disengaged!

But if you use the alternative key just once then the 'counter' is reset to zero and the process begins again. The solution to this potentially confusing procedure is to swap ignition keys on a regular basis. Of course, in reality this does not happen. Owners tuck the spare key away in a drawer somewhere and forget about it or, worse still, lose it altogether.

So, if you inadvertently reach the operational limit of the system the only way to get round the system is to take the car to the nearest dealer so that the system can be re-encrypted. This will cost you money – for the re-setting and the towing – so is best avoided! Bear this in mind also if considering buying a secondhand Laguna with just one key!

NEXT MONTH
MGF fault-finding

ELECTRONIC DIAGNOSTICS!

Tracing and fixing faults in electronic engine management systems

Number 39: *The MGF boasts a state-of-the-art Rover MEMS engine management system. Although it's early days yet as far as problems are concerned, Chris Graham discovers that the future could be interesting.*

Rover's MGF is an interesting vehicle in many respects, not least because of its mid-engined configuration – a million miles away from the traditional, front-engined MG layout. There are two versions of the car available at present and each has a different engine management system.

As Frank Massey, proprietor of Preston-based Fuel Injection Services (Tel: 01772 201597) explains, both are Rover MEMS-based but distinctly different. The 'entry level' car, with the straightforward 1.8-litre, multipoint injected engine uses a version denoted '1.9' (not to be confused with the engine size!). On the quick MGF, the car with the variable valve control system (VVC), you will find MEMS 2J engine management.

A significant difference between the

POSSIBLE FAULTS
1. **Injector fouling**
2. **Throttle pot**
3. **Distributor**

Car supplied by:
Syd Brown & Sons, Berry Lane, Longridge, Preston, Lancs. PR3 3NH.

two systems is that 1.9 features conventional ignition with coil, rotor arm and distributor cap etc., while 2J utilises a wasted spark (double-ended coil) set-up with a coil pack mounted at the front of the engine.

Also of note is the fact that the 2J system features an external MAP sensor, mounted on the inlet manifold. On the 1.9 version this sensor is located internally within the ECU, which is more in keeping with most previous MEMS systems.

For the purposes of this feature we decided to focus on the 1.9 MEMS version used on the 'basic' MGF, assuming that this would probably be the more common vehicle. It is currently about £2,500 cheaper than the VVC car and costs less to insure too!

PREPARATION

This is a bit of an unknown quantity from a practical point of view, simply because the car is still so new. It's early days yet and the car we looked at here showed no obvious signs of problems, apart from some evidence of dirt build-up on the distributor cap. The vehicle had covered just 4,500 miles.

Despite the MGF's long service intervals, Frank believes there is no excuse for neglect. He still advocates the regular inspection and washing out of

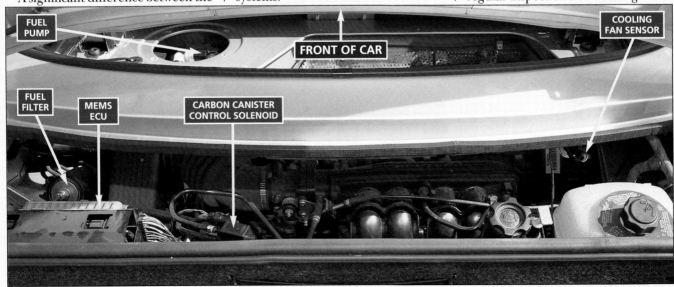

ENGINE MANAGEMENT

Gaining access to the engine on the MGF is the first problem. It posed real difficulties from a picture point of view as well! Main access is via the rear of the passenger compartment. The rear screen and hood must be detached and folded back and then a section of carpet which covers the rear parcel shelf removed. With this clear a bolted-down steel plate is revealed and, beneath this is the engine.

Removing the plate affords access to the whole of the top of the engine and, via a separate round access plate, to the fuel pump. In some respects Frank considers this system more convenient than a conventional front-engined layout because the whole set-up has been designed with the limited access problem in mind. However, he adds that it's not all plain sailing. Both the crank angle sensor and the Lambda sensor are rather tricky to get at.

For dealing with the more routine maintenance aspects of this engine there is a second access option found within the boot. Removing a simple metal ventilation grille allows for the checking of factors such as fluid levels, oil etc. In this case the ECU is a traditional component with a 36-pin MEMS socket. It should be noted that VVC-equipped cars feature a dual socket control unit – an obvious distinguishing factor.

Among the primary components used in this application are: a traditional two-wire inductive pick-up crank angle sensor to the rear of the flywheel which feeds directly to the ECU; a standard NTC coolant sensor found next to the thermostat housing; a knock sensor in the centre of the block (although we could not see it in this case); a multi-function unit (relay pack) on the nearside of the engine bay close to the ECU. This contains a number of relays but the downside of this layout is that if just one fails, the whole pack has to be renewed.

Interestingly, there are two air temperature sensors. One is a conventional ambient air type used to sample the temperature of the intake air in the traditional manner. The other measures the temperature within the engine bay itself. This is an important factor on this car because the engine is completely enclosed and relies on the operation of an electronic fan to draw air in through a side vent when the temperature reaches a pre-determined limit.

Other components include a simple push-button inertia switch on the nearside inner rear wing; a traditional stepper motor for engine idle speed control, fitted to the throttle body; a throttle potentiometer; an oxygen (Lambda) sensor fitted at the front of the engine and protected from excessive heat build up by some aluminised sheeting; a catalytic converter; a carbon canister (which

Frank noticed was a Vauxhall unit!) found on the nearside of the engine bay's rear bulkhead.

The engine runs on multipoint injection so there are four standard fuel injectors mounted on a standard fuel rail. A fuel pressure control regulator is located at the end of the rail, complete with a vacuum pipe to the inlet manifold.

The diagnostic socket is of the new 16-pin J1962 type, in common with most modern applications now. It is located in the fuse box just above the driver's footwell and allows for the extraction of fault codes and serial data plus the driving of actuators and the clearing of logged codes.

One other significant maintenance-related point on this application concerns service intervals. We have discovered that the change interval for the spark plugs is a whopping 60,000 miles, on both engine versions – assuming platinum plugs are used. As a general rule, Frank is not a supporter of 'fitting and forgetting' spark plugs for this sort of duration. He considers it very prudent to remove and check them on a regular basis, despite the official recommendation to do otherwise.

Also of note is the lengthy change interval for the cambelt – 72,000 miles on VVC cars, 90,000 on the standard engine. Time will tell if this is justified...

the throttle body with carburettor cleaner. Make sure the throttle disc remains clean and deposit-free.

On previous MEMS applications that we have considered, the MAP sensor pipe commonly proved a weak link. It often suffered with the ingress of oil and/or fuel which would sit in the tube to have a detrimental effect on the pulse signals being sent to the ECU. Consequently, Frank thinks that in this case it would be sensible to remove this pipe during routine servicing work and

blow it gently through with compressed air. However, be warned; never to do this in the direction of the ECU because you run the risk of causing serious and expensive internal damage.

The MAP sensor pipe itself is made from nylon which will effectively resist the long term effects of heat and will not decay. However, there are rubber sections at either end which may well deteriorate with time.

Without wishing to be over critical of the materials chosen, Frank does have

some worries about the longevity of selected vacuum hoses used on this engine. Remember that the confinement of the whole unit is likely to generate tremendous heat – much more than in a conventional under bonnet installation, placing extra strain on all rubberised and plastic pipework.

The integrity of the vacuum hoses is particularly critical on this application. Possible problems are that the pipes might lose their surface tension at the ends where they seal on to the components, plus they might suffer from cracking. Electrical wiring may undergo similar problems in the long term as well, from a combination of engine movement and extreme heating. Only time will tell but Frank says that, from his experience of mid-engine set-ups, these sorts of problem do eventually arise.

As far as actual component failure is concerned, he says that most are pretty durable these days even under these harsh conditions. So he doesn't see any potential problems in this respect.

One other surprising factor for Frank is that the designers did not specify lateral-fed fuel injectors for this application. One of the primary benefits of this type of injector is that the greater fuel flow, compared with conventional designs, improves cooling and the hot start performance of the engine. He can foresee fuel vaporisation problems as a consequence with the MGF. What's more, the fuel tank is located immediately ahead of the engine and Frank wonders if heat transfer may lead to problems in this respect

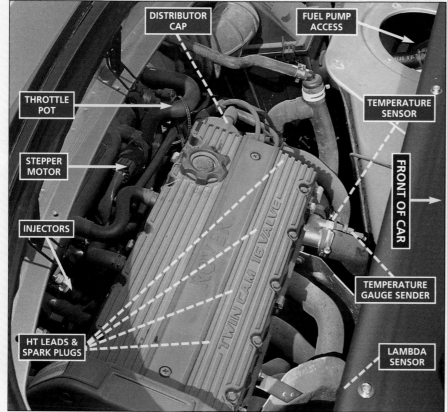

ELECTRONIC DIAGNOSTICS!

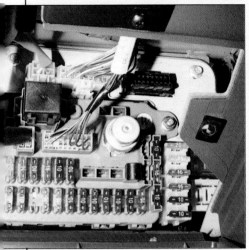

The diagnostic socket is tucked away next to the fuse board in the driver's footwell. It is the black, multi-pin socket seen here top right.

jectors (pintel tips). These sticky contaminants are liberated from the fuel under conditions of high temperature – when the car is stopped at a motorway service station, for example.

The practical symptoms can be hesitation and slight misfire problems at lower mileages than might normally be expected. Fortunately, the injectors are easy to remove and test so putting the problem right, should it arise, will be neither difficult nor expensive.

The throttle potentiometer is a constantly moving component. On sports car applications this is often more aggressively used than on a saloon, because of the nature of the driving, and this 'enthusiasm' may well lead to aggravated throttle pot. wear. The consequence is usually hesitation and flat spots because of the breakdown of the output track. This is easy to pick-up, check and to change.

We mentioned in the preparation notes that the distributor cap may be prone to surface contamination and that is should not be ignored over a long period of time. Frank can see the possibility of misfires and poor plug performance being caused by this condition if it is allowed to develop. He also raised a question mark over the longevity of the plug leads. These are found deep in the engine and so have to endure very high temperatures.

A knock-on consequence of injector fouling is that the lambda sensor will detect that insufficient fuel is being supplied and so its switching action will be affected and it will loose efficiency.

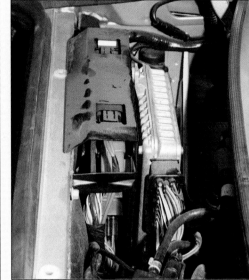

It will be interesting to see how the ECU copes with the extremes of temperature which are bound to occur within the engine compartment.

This may well lead to excess emission problems.

The lambda sensor used in this case is a heated component and it is always a good idea to check that it is switching at the correct frequency. Also make sure that the heater circuit is working.

The quality of engine oil is paramount too. With a multi-valve engine like this, Frank is not keen to see change intervals rise much above 10,000 miles, even when using the best synthetic products available, despite what the manufacturers say. Changing frequently is not a cheap policy but, in terms of the total value of the car, is does provide very cheap insurance against engine problems.

Many of the previous MEMS systems have suffered with a mysterious battery flattening problem according to Frank. He says that the cause is that the management system needs the ECU to remain powered up for about eight seconds after the ignition has been switched off, to give the idle control stepper motor time to be 'parked' in a suitable position ready for when the engine is next started.

The circuit which controls this main relay switching can fail internally within the ECU. The ground control circuit, which is actually the pull-down circuit for the main relay to the MEMS ECU, fails to disconnect and so the whole system is left powered up.

FUTURE PROBLEMS?

as well. Finally, it's interesting to note that the radiator is found at the front of the car and the steel connecting pipes between it and the engine run under the car, fully exposed to the elements. Frank considers that this will certainly bring down engine temperature, particularly under winter conditions. Thinking about the way this management system works, he wonders whether this may have an effect on engine fuelling in very cold weather. He believes that there is a possibility that the system may revert to partial cold start enrichment.

Because the MGF is still such a new vehicle nothing of a serious nature has come to light as yet. However, with one eye on the types of problem which afflict slightly older Rover models with similar engines and management systems, Frank is able to speculate here about some of the possible problems which may occur in due course with the MGF.

His first concern is that the heat generated in the engine compartment, due to the sealed-in nature of the installation, is likely to lead to premature fuel injector fouling. Commonly this is caused by lacquer and varnish-type materials being deposited on the in-

TECHNICAL SPECIFICATIONS

Crank angle sensor	Output – 2V peak to peak, 12V+ at cruise (pin 31) Earth return (pin 32) Screen – 0.25V max (pin 29)
Air temp. sensor	Output – 3V @ 20°C, 0.75V @ 80°C (pin 16) Return earth (pin 30) Reference voltage – 5V on pin 16
Coolant temp. sensor	Output – 3V @ 20°C, 0.75V @ 80°C (pin 33) Sensor return – 0.25V (pin 30) Reference voltage – 5V on pin 33
Oxygen sensor	Output – 0.2-0.8V @ 1Hz+
Throttle pos. indicator	Output – 0.5V closed, 4,5V open ((pin 8) Supply – 5V (pin 9) Earth – 0.25V (pin 30)
Idle stepper motor	Supply from main relay, terminal 87 Control on ECU pins 2, 3, 22 and 27 ground Control pulsed 12V to ground
Injectors duration	Hot – 2.2ms at idle, 5ms+ during cranking Cold – 3-3.5ms at idle, 10ms+ during cranking
Fuel flow	80+ ltr/min
Fuel pressure	2 bar with vac 2.5 bar without vac

THE SERIES SO FAR

BASIC SYSTEMS – July 1994 DIAGNOSTIC EQUIPMENT – August 1994 TEST PREPARATION – September 1994 FORD 2.0I – October 1994 ROVER 200/400 – November 1994 VAUXHALL 2.0i – December 1994 PEUGEOT 205/309 GTI – January 1995 FORD 2.9i V6 – February 1995 BMW 1.8i – March 1995 VAUXHALL 2.0i 16V – April 1995 ROVER 2.0i 16V – May 1995 ROVER 1.6/2.0 EFi – June 1995 ROVER 1.6/2.0 IGNITION – July 1995 FORD ZETA 16V – August 1995 VW 1.8 DIGIFANT – September 1995 HONDA LEGEND/ROVER 800 – October 1995 FORD XR2i/RS TURBO – November 1995 PEUGEOT 405 Mi16 – December 1995 RENAULT CLIO 1.2i – January 1996 VAUXHALL 24V – February 1996 RANGE ROVER V8 – March 1996 HONDA CIVIC 1.6 – April 1996 ROVER 820 SINGLE POINT – May 1996 JAGUAR 3.6 STRAIGHT SIX – June 1996 AUDI 80 – July 1996 FORD ESCORT/FIESTA – August 1996 VAUXHALL 1.8i – September 1996 SAAB 900/9000 – November 1996 VW DIGIFANT UPDATE – December 1996 VAUXHALL ECOTEC – January 1997 NISSAN MICRA 16V – February 1997 PEUGEOT 1.8i – March 1997 VOLVO 940 2.0 – April 1997 FIAT PUNTO 1.2 – May 1997 BMW 24V – June 1997 CITROEN AX – July 1997 NISSAN PRIMERA – August 1997 RENAULT LAGUNA 2.0 – September 1997.

This is the twin coil pack used by the MEMS 2J system found on VVC MGFs.

While this does not cause an immediate problem for the car, the electrical drain can be sufficient to flatten the battery within eight hours or so. Diagnosing the problem is not difficult, but putting it right requires the purchase of a new ECU. Now in this case Frank is unable to say whether the MGF will suffer similarly but time will tell. On other Rover MEMS applications it has been an age-related condition.

One other previously experienced MEMS ECU-related problem has been with the internal MAP sensor – as found on the standard car but not on the VVC version. These go out of range and become unable to sample the pressure pulse correctly, causing either timing anomalies (slow ignition advance) or incorrect fuel supply to the injectors.

Again this tends to be an age-related condition and one which Frank's experience suggests strikes at around the

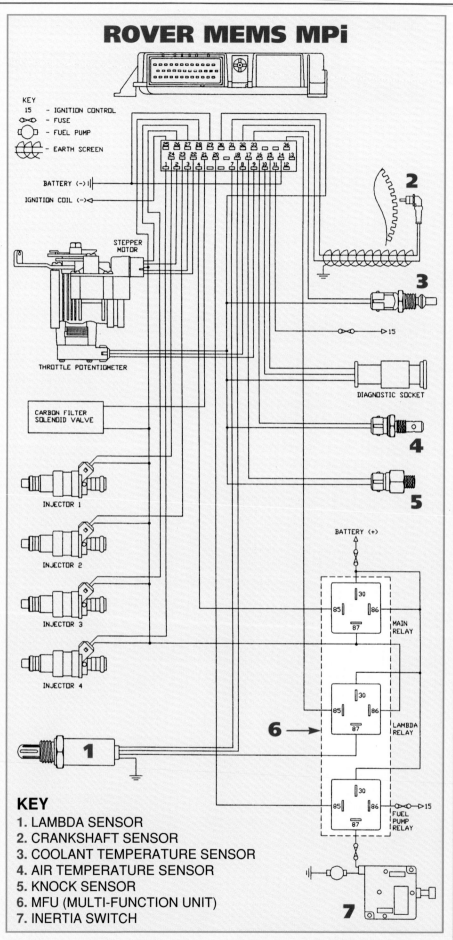

ROVER MEMS MPi

KEY
15 – IGNITION CONTROL
– FUSE
– FUEL PUMP
– EARTH SCREEN

BATTERY (–)
IGNITION COIL (–)

STEPPER MOTOR

THROTTLE POTENTIOMETER

CARBON FILTER SOLENOID VALVE

INJECTOR 1
INJECTOR 2
INJECTOR 3
INJECTOR 4

DIAGNOSTIC SOCKET

BATTERY (+)

MAIN RELAY

LAMBDA RELAY

FUEL PUMP RELAY

KEY

1. LAMBDA SENSOR
2. CRANKSHAFT SENSOR
3. COOLANT TEMPERATURE SENSOR
4. AIR TEMPERATURE SENSOR
5. KNOCK SENSOR
6. MFU (MULTI-FUNCTION UNIT)
7. INERTIA SWITCH

60,000 mile mark, if at all. Because the MAP sensor is within the ECU there is no possibility for repair and a new unit is the only option. Fortunately, refurbished MEMS ECUs are not expensive by modern standards and can be pur-

chased from the likes of ATP (Tel: 01543 467466) for about £120.

NEXT MONTH

Escort Cosworth

ELECTRONIC DIAGNOSTICS!

Tracing and fixing faults in electronic engine management systems

Number 40: *This month we get to grips with the fastest Ford of the lot, the turbocharged nerve-tingler that is the Escort Cosworth! Chris Graham reports.*

Love 'em or hate 'em, there is no denying the sheer driving thrill to be had at the wheel of a Cosworth-powered Ford – be it a Sierra, Sapphire or Escort. Each offers near supercar performance for saloon car money. But what other costs are involved? Are these engines up to the job, and what problems occur?

The man with all the answers, electronics and tuning supremo Frank

POSSIBLE FAULTS
1. **Engine misfires**
2. **Phase sensor**
3. **Coolant sensor**

Massey (Fuel Injection Services, Tel: 01772 201597), remains surprisingly optimistic about the overall durability of these high performance family flyers. He has nothing but praise for the strength of the engine itself, the qual-

ity of the components used and the ultimate reliability and efficiency of the Weber IAW management system which runs the show.

The combination is a well proven one which lasts, assuming it is looked after. Unfortunately, what tends to upset these cars most of all is 'inappropriate' tuning. There are many 'specialists' who will modify engines to produce tremendous power outputs, well

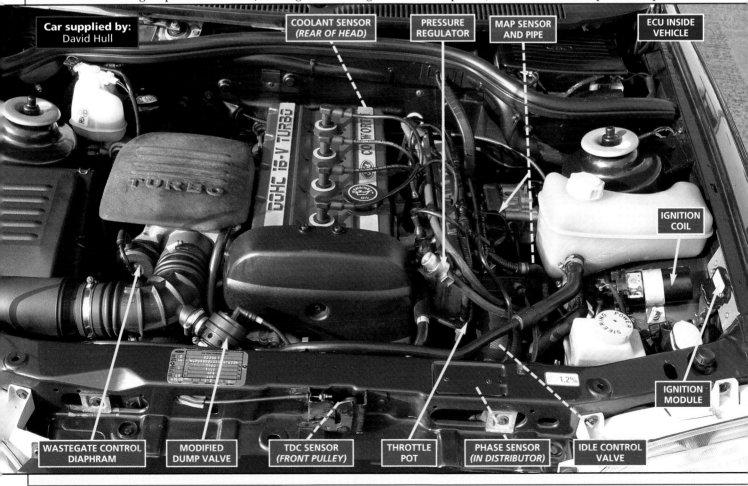

Car supplied by: David Hull

COOLANT SENSOR (REAR OF HEAD)

PRESSURE REGULATOR

MAP SENSOR AND PIPE

ECU INSIDE VEHICLE

IGNITION COIL

IGNITION MODULE

WASTEGATE CONTROL DIAPHRAM

MODIFIED DUMP VALVE

TDC SENSOR (FRONT PULLEY)

THROTTLE POT

PHASE SENSOR (IN DISTRIBUTOR)

IDLE CONTROL VALVE

ENGINE MANAGEMENT

Weber IAW is a full-blown engine management system, controlling both ignition and fuelling from one a single, 35-pin ECU. It utilises an external ignition amplifier module linked to a conventional ignition coil, and relies on the three traditional inputs – load, speed and temperature – for its function.

The system has been around for about ten years now on Ford applications, appearing first on the earliest Cosworth Sierras. It can also be found on selected Fiat and Lancia models, plus Ducatti motor cycles. Its use with Ford is restricted to Cosworth variants.

It is a multipoint system with four injectors working sequentially, although on the high-spec RS 500 versions there are actually eight injectors! The second four are brought into action under hard acceleration.

The system has changed only marginally over the years. Some of the components used and their locations have been altered but, essentially, the workings have remained the same. The ECU is located inside the car, behind the passenger glove box.

Components to be found on the Escort Cosworth consist of: a Lambda sensor in the exhaust downpipe; a TDC (position) sensor externally-mounted on the front pulley; a dis-tributor containing a phase sensor for timing the injectors (producing just two off-set pulses) and a simple rotor arm.

There are two main relays (one for the ECU, injectors, turbo wastegate control valve and idle control valve; the other for the fuel pump) a charcoal canister with valve; a separate ignition module which is responsible for switching the coil upon direct instruction from the ECU.

In addition, there is a traditional NTC, two-wire coolant sensor found at the back of the head; an air temperature sensor in the main air induction pipe; an octane adjust socket; a wastegate control valve mounted at the front of the engine which diverts pressure from the turbo to control boost. This is electronically controlled by the ECU.

Also present are: a two-wire idle control valve (plunge type); an adjustable, three-wire throttle position sensor which is a potentiometer rather than a switch and works in the traditional manner (in most cases starts at a low voltage and goes high); a MAP sensor to monitor engine load.

Because this engine has a turbo, the MAP sensor has to be capable of operating in two directions to accommodate negative and positive pressure. The atmospheric value is half-way through the range. This component has to be changed to cope with the greater boost pressures encountered when the engine is modified.

The injectors are solenoid-operated and are essentially conventional. They are directly driven by the ECU and are very high flow units – almost double the rate of fuel of the typical unit normally found on a standard two-litre engine.

The system is code readable. A self-test connector, which is a three-pin socket, allows for the use of a code reader. In this way fault code information can be accessed but these are two-digit codes only and so limited in their usefulness. Consequently, Frank places little emphasis on this from a diagnostics point of view. No data can be read.

It is the operation of the wastegate control valve which many people tamper with. Leaving closed for longer increases boost pressure and ups the power output of the engine. There is a built-in safety mechanism within the ECU which cuts fuel injection if boost pressure exceeds a pre-set limit. Many less sophisticated modification packages simply override this mechanism and remove all the safety protection. This places undue mechanical stress on the engine – it drives to destruction very quickly!

---

in excess of the standard 220hp. While this can be done very successfully by experienced tuners, getting it wrong can be disastrous.

Despite the 1993 Escort used in the pictures here, much of the content of this feature is equally applicable to earlier Cosworths. The management system has altered little over the production run so the typical failings detailed here can be related across the board.

PREPARATION

Much depends upon the general condition of the engine. However, assuming an average, genuine vehicle, Frank's approach is first to remove and inspect the plug leads. These pass deep into the head and must be in good, intact condition. The rubber insulation will become brittle with age and, if cracks occur, electrical tracking will result. The plugs too must be 'spot on' so remove and check these also.

It is vital that plug range and electrode gap are correct. Never skimp on plug quality. Frank's preference is for NGK platinum plugs. Under turbo boost conditions compression is increased so the leads have to be electronically secure and the gap correct if the plug is to fire properly.

Remove the distributor cap, inspect and clean as necessary. Generally these stay clean on this application but it's worth checking anyway. They can be fiddly and awkward to remove, so sometimes they get ignored.

The TDC centre at the front of the engine is totally exposed and this, coupled with the fact that it is a magnetic component, ensures that it catches everything that life throws at it. Wash it with a brush and cleaning solution and dry it thoroughly afterwards.

Remove the hose which connects the intercooler to the main air intake for the engine. This is a short hose with a diameter of about three inches. This will provide access for cleaning the throttle butterfly, and checking that its stop is correctly set. This should just hold the butterfly off the body, and no more. Incorrect adjustment here will directly affect the voltage output from the potentiometer, so it must be right.

Although the engine's idle speed is governed by the plunge-type idle control valve, there is a manual bleed valve as well, which actually sets base idle. This is found directly under the throttle body and is easily spotted with the hose removed. Use this to set the idle speed once the throttle stop is correctly adjusted, if it is not correct already.

The idle control valve is secured by two screws so is easy to remove. Wash it thoroughly with carburettor cleaner and lubricate with a squirt of WD40.

Make a careful check of all the rubber hoses around the turbo. Do this when the engine is cold for obvious reasons – turbos get extremely hot! Inspect all the pipes running between the turbo, the intercooler and the engine. These tend to get oily, softened with age and weak. Air leaks of any sort will result in lost performance as turbo pressure will drop.

Low boost pressure can, of course, be caused by a problem with the turbo, but the integrity of these pipes can be at the root as well. The system is essentially a difficult one to check because it is only under pressure when the turbo is on boost. If in any doubt change the hoses.

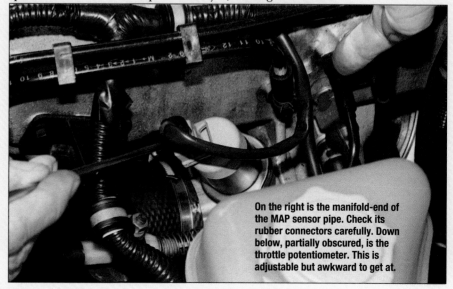

On the right is the manifold-end of the MAP sensor pipe. Check its rubber connectors carefully. Down below, partially obscured, is the throttle potentiometer. This is adjustable but awkward to get at.

ELECTRONIC DIAGNOSTICS!

Remember also that the intercooler, which is basically an air radiator, can become contaminated with oil. This greatly reduces its efficiency. Remove it, soak it in detergent, rinse with a pressure washer and dry itq thoroughly.

While checking the hoses to the turbo, it is worth inspecting the impeller too. This should rotate freely. If you can't spin it with a flick of the finger then there is probably a bush wear problem. Expect to feel free play in the impeller. This is quite normal when the unit is cold. However, with age it can become excessive, causing the blades to scrap the inside of the housing with a characteristic clatter or squealing noise. If this is the case then the turbo must be replaced.

The other give-away of excessive bearing movement will be an oily turbo with burnt carbon evident on the impellers. Frank is reluctant to carry out this level of investigation as a matter of course during normal preparation. He restricts it to cases when high oil consumption is reported or when the exhaust is very smoky.

Finally, it is important to inspect the small pipe which runs between the inlet manifold and the MAP sensor. This is a critical component. Although the centre section of the pipe is rigid plastic, the two ends are soft rubber. It features two right-angled bends and can collect oil within. This will affect its operation, as will deformation of the plastic ends. Any distortion or blockage can cause dramatic driveability problems.

COSSIE COMPLAINTS

The MAP sensor output on this application is absolutely critical and is well worth checking for that reason. Fluctuations in output are reasonably common according to Frank and will present themselves often as violent driveability problems – commonly shuddering and hesitation. These usually strike under conditions of high turbo boost, when the throttle has been floored!

The most common cause of this is nothing more than a misfire at the plug. An engine misfire can be caused by many different factors, such as poor leads, a dirty distrib-utor cap, a faulty plug. Any of these will be sufficient to create a reverse pressure pulse in the air intake system. This fluctuation finds its way to the MAP sensor which responds in turn to have a direct and immediate effect on engine fuelling.

It is true to say that assuming good basic preparation has been carried out, the presence of misfires should not be an issue. However, Frank says it does occur reasonably often, probably because the potential causes are so many and varied. Two very common causes are the wrong type of plug being fitted, and the incorrect gap being set.

As we have already mentioned, there is a phase sensor within the distributor and problems with this are extremely common. In fact, it's not actually the sensor itself, but its connections. There are two wires and both are notorious for becoming brittle and eventually breaking.

The result is very poor performance, intermittently to start with, as the wires break down. Franks says that if the ECU detects this type of phase sensor problem then it reverts to a 'limp home' mode until the engine is switched off. Upon restart everything is reset and performance returns until higher engine speeds are hit, when injection phasing is again required, and the problem repeats itself.

This is a known fault with this Weber

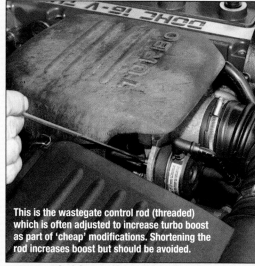

This is the wastegate control rod (threaded) which is often adjusted to increase turbo boost as part of 'cheap' modifications. Shortening the rod increases boost but should be avoided.

system. If either wire is found to be brittle then the sensor must be replaced without question. Frank says that these are not available singly from Ford, and that a whole distributor has to be purchased. However, a trip to your local Fiat dealer will produce an individual and identical sensor!

Checking the phase sensor requires a quality oscilloscope because the component produces a relatively small sine wave. However, diagnosis can be complicated by the often intermittent nature of the problem. The ideal solution is to fit a breakout box and drive the car with a hand-held scope connected.

A further subtlety is that problems may also arise not because a component has actually failed, but because it is operating slightly out of range. This can be sufficient to generate fuelling and ignition problems and can only be detected by detailed analysis of the operating ranges.

If the MAP sensor is more that 0.5V out, for example, this will have a critical effect on performance. The same applies to the voltage from the coolant temperature sensor and the throttle potentiometer. In some cases poor wiring condition can be sufficient to set up such deviations, but usually it is a problem with the component itself and so replacement is the only solution.

Check the phase sensor's socket for dirt contamination as well. This is located right at the front of the engine, next to the socket for TDC sensor. Because of this position it can be prone to dirt and water thrown up from the road. Clean the socket carefully and treat with a quality, silicone-based lubricant to prevent further problems.

Another component failure, this time with the

TECHNICAL SPECIFICATIONS

Crank angle sensor (ECU pin 3/4)	Sine wave, 10V peak to peak Cranking 5V peak to peak
Phase sensor (ECU pin 23/5)	10V peak to peak, 2 pulses (offset) Cranking 5V peak to peak
Trigger to amp (ECU pin 25)	5V digital
Injector pulse (ECU 35/32/33/18)	Hot 2.5ms, cold 3-4ms, (Surge and hold cold cranking 8-10ms pattern)
Throttle pot (ECU pin 17)	0.3-4.5V with throttle open
Coolant sensor (ECU pin 29)	3.5V cold, 0.5V hot
Air temp sensor (ECU pin 31)	Approx 3.0V at 20°C
MAP sensor	Atmos 2.25V, 20in/Hg 0.75V (idle) 2.6V at 3psi, 4.5V at 15psi
Idle control valve (ECU pin 34)	12V digital, CB neg (Amp pin 7)
Wastegate control (ECU pin 16)	12V digital when active

THE SERIES SO FAR

BASIC SYSTEMS – July 1994 DIAGNOSTIC EQUIPMENT – August 1994 TEST PREPARATION – September 1994 FORD 2.0i – October 1994 ROVER 200/400 – November 1994 VAUXHALL 2.0i – December 1994 PEUGEOT 205/309 GTi – January 1995 FORD 2.9i V6 – February 1995 BMW 1.8i – March 1995 VAUXHALL 2.0i 16V – April 1995 ROVER 2.0i 16V – May 1995 ROVER 1.6/2.0 EFi – June 1995 ROVER 1.6/2.0 IGNITION – July 1995 FORD ZETA 16V – August 1995 VW 1.8 DIGIFANT – September 1995 HONDA LEGEND/ROVER 800 – October 1995 FORD XR2i/RS TURBO – November 1995 PEUGEOT 405 Mi16 – December 1995 RENAULT CLIO 1.2i – January 1996 VAUXHALL 24V – February 1996 RANGE ROVER V8 – March 1996 HONDA CIVIC 1.6 – April 1996 ROVER 820 SINGLE POINT – May 1996 JAGUAR 3.6 STRAIGHT SIX – June 1996 AUDI 80 – July 1996 FORD ESCORT/FIESTA – August 1996 VAUXHALL 1.8i – September 1996 SAAB 900/9000 – November 1996 VW DIGIFANT UPDATE – December 1996 VAUXHALL ECOTEC – January 1997 NISSAN MICRA 16V – February 1997 PEUGEOT 1.8i – March 1997 VOLVO 940 2.0 – April 1997 FIAT PUNTO 1.2 – May 1997 BMW 24V – June 1997 CITROEN AX – July 1997 NISSAN PRIMERA – August 1997 RENAULT LAGUNA 2.0 – September 1997 MGF – October 1997.

coolant sensor, can be an additional cause of trouble. This tends to be an age-related complaint and the most recent example encountered by Frank showed the sensor to be failing midway through its range. The car would perform perfectly well from cold but, as the engine warmed up, the sensor went 'open circuit' and the mixture went extremely rich. Frank said there was no fail-safe value built in for this sensor so fuelling was shot to pieces. Once the engine was fully warm, the sensor failed intermittently with consequent derivability problems. Heat and vibration seemed to affect it, the exhaust became very smoky and the car did not perform well through the mid range. Under hard acceleration, on full boost, performance returned.

A knock-on consequence of this was that the plugs became fouled, leading to misfires and the additional problems described above. The effects of coolant sensor failure are quite easy to find. Injector duration becomes obviously extended and provides the simplest tell-tale symptom.

Finally, spare a thought for the turbo. One particular problem can be a sudden loss of power under hard acceleration. One possibility is that the wastegate actuator has been fiddled with to increase boost pressure but the ECU has not been modified accordingly. Consequently, when the ECU's pre-programmed turbo boost limit is breached, it simply acts to protect the engine by cutting off the fuel supply! Use a pressure gauge during a road test to confirm the boost pressure. If it goes higher than 0.8 bar then this will be sufficient to trip the ECU.

NEXT MONTH
Citroën Xantia

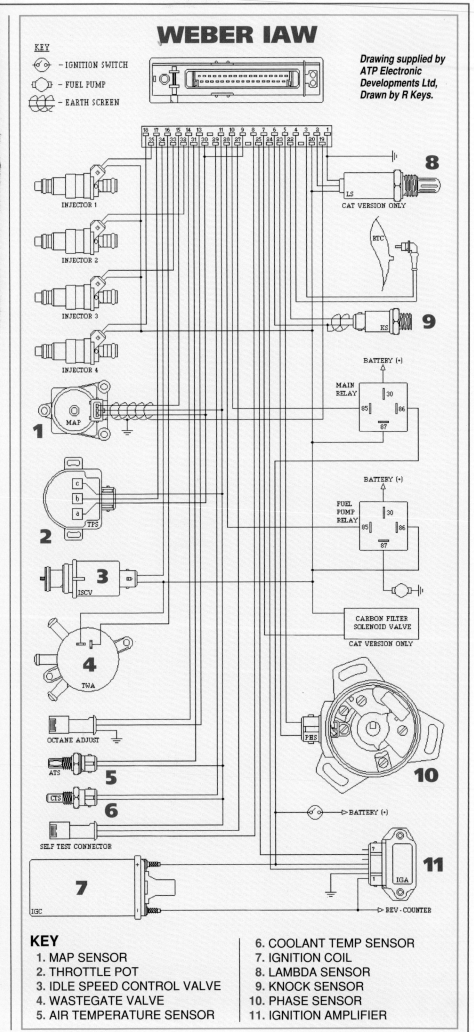

WEBER IAW

Drawing supplied by ATP Electronic Developments Ltd, Drawn by R Keys.

KEY
- ⊘ – IGNITION SWITCH
- ⊟ – FUEL PUMP
- ⊜ – EARTH SCREEN

INJECTOR 1
INJECTOR 2
INJECTOR 3
INJECTOR 4

1 MAP
2 TPS
3 ISCV
4 TWA
OCTANE ADJUST
5 ATS
6 CTS
SELF TEST CONNECTOR
7 IGC

8 LS CAT VERSION ONLY
KTC
9 KS
BATTERY (+)
MAIN RELAY 30 85 86 87
BATTERY (+)
FUEL PUMP RELAY 30 85 86 87
CARBON FILTER SOLENOID VALVE CAT VERSION ONLY
10 PHS
BATTERY (+)
11 IGA
REV-COUNTER

18 17 16 15 14 13 11 9 8 7 6 5 4 3 2 1
35 34 33 32 31 30 29 28 27 25 24 23 22 20 19

KEY

1. MAP SENSOR
2. THROTTLE POT
3. IDLE SPEED CONTROL VALVE
4. WASTEGATE VALVE
5. AIR TEMPERATURE SENSOR
6. COOLANT TEMP SENSOR
7. IGNITION COIL
8. LAMBDA SENSOR
9. KNOCK SENSOR
10. PHASE SENSOR
11. IGNITION AMPLIFIER